The litt

BIG
BEAUTY™

The information contained in this book is of a general nature only.
If you wish to make use of any information in this book relating to your
health, you should first consider its appropriateness to your situation,
including consulting a medical professional.

PENGUIN BOOKS

UK | USA | Canada | Ireland | Australia
India | New Zealand | South Africa | China

Penguin Books is part of the Penguin Random House group of companies
whose addresses can be found at global.penguinrandomhouse.com.

Penguin
Random House
Australia

First published by Penguin Random House Australia 2018

Text copyright © Bernadette Fisers 2018

The moral right of the author has been asserted.

Text and cover design by Myrtle Jeffs © Penguin Random House Australia
Typeset in Helvetica Neue by Myrtle Jeffs
People illustrations © Leremy Gan
Product illustrations © Ashley Barbieri
Author photograph by Terence Langendoen
Printed and bound in China by RR Donnelley Asia Printing Solutions Limited

A catalogue record for this
book is available from the
National Library of Australia

ISBN 978 0 14379 169 0

penguin.com.au

The little book of

BIG

BEAUTY™

by Bernadette Fisers

for my mum, claire, who has always
shown me the beauty in the world.

contents

64
beautiful
habits

85
outer beauty
the knowledge you need

hi
beautiful
:)

the changing
face of beauty

Why do so many of us feel it's important for us to be thought of as beautiful? We're prepared to paint ourselves, inject ourselves and spend a small fortune in the search for attractiveness. There is a massive industry that I have been working in for over thirty years that pays homage at the shrine of beauty, while women worldwide offer themselves up to it on a daily basis. And me? I'm a believer, a devotee who practises daily. But when we stop to think about it, are we doing it for ourselves? Are we doing it to compete with others? Or are there romantic reasons behind our continual quest?

The idea of the value of beauty is not new by any means – it's been around forever. We've been grooming ourselves since the dawn of time, and without question one of the driving forces in this mission is to find a mate. Many of us believe that if we are more beautiful, we will have a better chance of success in that area – and possibly there is some truth to that. But people were born not only with eyes, but with ears as well. Take Cleopatra, who was admired for her strength of character as much as for her beauty. We require much more than a 'look'; we need a total package that combines inner strengths with outer beauty, and a healthy attitude to beauty means working on both.

I've seen many women in London hurriedly applying their makeup on the train to work – a mini mirror, a makeup bag and they're set – while in Australia and the USA it's common to see application happening in the car. It's a sign of status to whip out a gold-plated lipstick and start coating our lips. A designer name and chic packaging are all we need to feel important. We're paying for packaging and we love it. We believe the marketing and we aspire to be like the models and celebrities who flog the products. We're buying the dream.

We spend hours at the makeup counters agonising over what colours will best suit us and magically transform our looks. We pay exorbitant amounts for miracle creams that claim to hold back time. These are mostly false claims made by a billion-dollar industry that loves to keep you on the brink of insecurity – in fact, that is exactly where it thrives and feeds. The more we feel 'less than', the more we will spend at the makeup counters to help us feel 'enough'. But in the search for that magic product we sometimes forget that true beauty is so much more than skin deep.

We become obsessed with particular products, thinking they are the only one for us – like having a crush, we feel as though we can't do without them. When our favourite products go out of stock or have been discontinued: disaster. We frantically search for a new one that might fill the void. If we only knew that there are many twins of the same product sitting on the shelves that will cost us less than the original. We'd just disregarded them because they seemed too cheap, too available.

Don't get me wrong, I absolutely love cosmetics and what they can do for a person. I love the transformations and the confidence boost that they can bring. I've just got past the bullshit. I know the truth and I've seen behind the curtain. There *is* magic – it's just not where you think it is.

I've spent my life applying makeup to various women, famous and not so famous. Women with egos so fragile that they cry with relief when looking in the mirror after I've finished. I'm always touched and humbled when this happens; it never fails to surprise me. This is the true magic.

We feel incomplete if we walk out the door without our makeup on. We hide in our bathrooms, sneak off to the mirror to 'fix' ourselves up. It takes time to look like this. We invest portions of our life staring into the mirror, constantly trying to improve our

i love the humour, intelligence, kindness and humility that truly beautiful people show.

appearance. Even though we're smarter than ever, we keep trying to fix without questioning whether there's anything really broken. We find swarms of young females staring in nightclub mirrors, bonding and beautifying at the same time. It's a universal theme that ends in a selfie.

Physical beauty means different things in various countries and it's also valued by each of us in our own unique way. It is truly in the eye of the beholder. Internal beauty is different – it's a worldwide human standard. We all appreciate kindness, humility, humour and respect. It speaks the same language no matter what country you are in. It doesn't vary with fashion. It just is. It's the type of beauty that doesn't come in a bottle, you can't buy it and you can't put it on – yet it's magnetic and memorable. It's truly valuable, and it's available to everyone.

Over the years our idea of beauty has changed countless times. It's hard to get a solid grip on it because it's a constantly moving target. We valued thin eyebrows in the '70s, bushy brows in the '80s and now it's all about highly defined, structured brows. If you believe the cosmetics ads, one minute you need a smoky eye and the next a natural look. What's changed is that

makeup and beauty styles are moving with fashion, and the fashion cycle has gone into warp speed. It's hard to keep up with the constant new trends that drive sales.

What is considered attractive also varies on different continents. We Aussies like to look tanned and fit and will spend endless hours baking at the beach or applying fake tan and hours more working out at the gym. In the UK a lot of people also want that golden glow: one whiff of sun and the Brits are half-naked in the park, baking their lilywhite bodies until they are painfully cherry-red.

In Japan, the sun is seen as damaging and the beautifully fashionable will walk around with an umbrella delicately shading their porcelain skin. Models heading to Asia for work want to be luminously white – lighter skin generally equals more work. Sometimes I think if they could glow in the dark they would! Whitening creams are bestsellers within the beauty market there, selling billions' worth every year.

Stretched earlobes and lips in parts of Africa are a sign of beauty, as is an elongated neck for the Kayan tribeswomen in Thailand. Henna drawn in intricate patterns is an Indian staple of

It's easy to see the beauty in a young child because they haven't yet learnt the art of deception or vanity – instead they possess a profound honesty and curiosity about the world. And imperfection can be beautiful – a small mouth and wide, clear eyes are not considered classically beautiful but can add up to the most stunning face.

Think of your friends: do you love them because of how they look? Unlikely. It's the combination of their personality traits that finds its way into your heart. Just like them, your looks are a small part of a much bigger picture.

beauty. We are all different in what we find externally beautiful and there is no universal rule – that's what makes the world so wonderful. It's not a beauty competition. How can you say a Renoir is more beautiful than a van Gogh?

We are all unique and we all matter. It makes no difference whether you are a businesswoman in Paris, a tailor in China or a Maasai mother in Africa: there is beauty in all of us. So I think that when looking at all these diverse signs of beauty there is really only one conclusion: be the best you possible, in every way.

So think: do you spend as much time on your inner beauty as your outer beauty? Do you know how to make the most of what you've got? Do you notice the beauty in the world that is right in front of you? If not, take a read – you just might find something that speaks to you.

If we can reframe our idea of beauty by taking a really honest look at it and brushing off the superficial aspects of it, we can all live with greater joy, confidence and meaning.

Because let's face it, we're worth it.

my beauty journey

Beauty has always been a big part of my life – the fascination began when I was tiny and it's been at the centre of my career ever since. My mum had a small makeup drawer in our tiny bathroom at home while I was growing up. It was a small, overworked room that served nine people – crazy busy – but tucked away in the '70s-style, faux marble cabinet with the ornate gold handles was a small treasure trove of makeup. Not the expensive kind, no designer labels in sight; just good, practical pieces that my mum could really use (plus lots of coral lipstick, for some weird obsessive coral-lipstick-loving reason!). This was makeup that worked exactly the same as if it had come from the most expensive cosmetics house.

I would stand and watch her carefully apply her makeup – she would always have to 'put her face on' if she was going out. There were expressions that accommodated particular items of makeup: the open mouth for putting on mascara, the half-closed eyes for foundation. I was riveted. In the bathroom mirror that was barely big enough to see her own face in, let alone my watchful one as well, the transformation would begin.

I suspect I really began my love affair with makeup when I met my grade two primary teacher, Miss Charmaine. She was a peacock in a world of black-and-white penguins at my local Catholic primary school, where most of the teachers were nuns. Miss Charmaine had the most amazing long, lacquered nails which she used to stroke her vibrant red hair, and her makeup was stunning and mesmerising to my six-year-old eyes. She certainly wasn't classically beautiful by any means, but it was what she did with what she had that was so amazing. It was my first girl crush.

By the time I was about twelve, my mum had worked out that I was actually pretty good at putting makeup on her, and she would call me into our cramped bathroom to do just that. My makeup career had begun. Once finished transforming, I would check to make sure that I had a happy and confident customer walking out the door.

I struck it rich when I was around thirteen, as my next-door neighbour, Mrs Tharle, hired me to set her fine lavender-coloured hair every week for the princely sum of $5. She said I did a better job than the local hairdresser, and I probably did – I was obsessed with getting it perfect. Just the right amount of Queen Elizabeth curl mixed with rock-star teasing, all finished off with a generous amount of super-hold hairspray that I sprayed madly whilst holding my breath.

I got a job at the local hair salon when I was about fourteen. I was underage and my parents had to sign a form acknowledging exactly that – that I was very young and very naïve. I started off washing hair in the men's department downstairs. I was completely terrible at it and many times the client would sit in the chair, naked from the waist up because I had soaked them so thoroughly. Meanwhile, their missing clothes were doing the speedy cycle in the clothes dryer. Woops.

I started my own little makeup collection when I was fifteen, just cheap makeup that I bought at a discount store. There was no slathering it on – I carefully applied it to enhance, not to cover. Even then, I knew the power of those little pots. I remember my high school PE teacher asking for makeup tips when she saw me applying it to myself in the swimming pool change rooms. I happily taught her why I chose a crème blush over powder – another satisfied customer.

My first full-time job was at a beautician's in Toorak. I beat 200 other eager applicants to get what I thought was the job of my dreams, but it turned out I worked a ridiculous – and probably illegal – seventy hours a week without much of a lunch break and very little money in my pay packet. It was probably the only time in my life I didn't have a weight issue because I never sat down – like, ever! I would fall asleep on the long journey home, gently rocked by the train. I was so exhausted.

Later on, I found a job working at the YSL counter in a large, elegant department store while I was studying makeup artistry full-time. My dad told me I was wasting my time and I should get a real job instead. It's funny in hindsight how wrong he was – makeup is my passion and I was not to be swayed. Almost all the girls from the other competing counters would come to me for their very own party makeup application, and I kept a tiny diary of rotating counter staff appointments. I was especially busy on a Friday and Saturday afternoon, getting them ready for their hot dates. My sales were crap, as I couldn't be bothered selling – in fact, I remember telling customers where they could get exactly the same product at a cheaper price. A big no-no in sales!

I eventually finished my makeup artistry course, passing with flying colours. I remember getting two of my sisters to be

models for my exams. One of them had to go back to her law offices with a blue face because I couldn't remove the face paint adequately, and the other ended up walking around the college half-naked because I assured her – in between gasps of laughter – that the body paint covered everything and that she really didn't need clothes at all . . . needless to say, it didn't. Hilarious, looking back now.

Then I managed to land a job with Opera Australia, helping out the two guys who ran the hair and makeup department. It was a great learning experience for me and they were generous in their encouragement and teaching. It paid like crap but I loved the creativeness, drama and colour of the theatre world, so I did it while earning some real money doing night shifts at a stockbrokers. Our makeup area was situated in the labyrinth of backstage rooms located underneath the arts centre. Opera singers and dancers would walk or dance in as mere humans and emerge as birds, statues, devils, heroes or whatever else was currently on the program. I can still see the rows of colourful tutus hanging overhead in the wardrobe department, waiting for their starring moment, and I really appreciated the great teamwork and talent that was behind any successful show.

Eventually, I took the plunge and devoted all of my time and efforts to makeup and hair. I've travelled the world with my skills. I've worked on rooftops in Hong Kong for magazines, islands in Italy for fashion campaigns and TV shows in Berlin. I've transformed famous singers, celebrities, actresses and models.

I've worked with great teams of creative people, from photographers to visionary art directors. We mostly work closely in small groups of people, discussing looks and fashion trends, working out the next big thing that's coming out of Paris or Milan. There are many private conversations held in the makeup mirror, and whatever's said in the makeup room stays precisely there. It's part counselling job and part therapy at times. Moods and relationships play a big part in the trust that goes on behind the scenes. Shoot teams often come together to work intensively for a week or so, never to see each other again for another year. We share amazing experiences in exotic locations. We can also spend the day on the beach freezing our arses off or sweltering in the desert with little shade in sight – we usually shoot winter wear in summer and summer wear in winter. It's an upside-down world and I love it all.

beauty is my
great passion,
and it's one i'm
now going to
share with you.

true beauty
is an essence.
it's not just how
you look nor how
you act, because
it's hard to see
one without
the other.

it's both – closely
intertwined.

inner
beauty
ways to be . . .

be authentic

you're already beautifully original – you just don't know it yet.

It takes me about thirty seconds to get over how you look. The reason it doesn't take long is because I have worked on some of the most beautiful faces and realised, over time, that beauty is not only about looks – it is so much more. It's about the person within, and when that person is being completely themselves that comes through, and we feel and appreciate their authenticity. The world is a beautifully diverse place with many different types of people in it and that's what makes it so wonderful. I appreciate the unique personalities I meet.

Not all the personalities I come across are genuine, though. I remember a popular celebrity who was visiting my home town and I was the 'lucky' makeup artist booked to work my magic on her. I knocked on her hotel door, only to be grabbed by the clothing stylist who was travelling with her – desperately mouthing the word 'help'. I dragged her into the hallway where she explained that the celeb, known for being bubbly and charming, was in fact a complete lunatic who had woken up the stylist during the night and thrown brushes at her. The unfortunate girl was now stuck in a foreign country with a madwoman. Yep . . . not at all like her media profile. Infinitely disappointing and flat-out crazy.

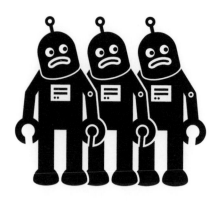

Authenticity is about being genuine and real, not false. It's being the true you as much as possible, and definitely not about just giving people what they want to see. And that's hard to do – we all have various people and expectations constantly tugging us in all directions. Possibly you're a different 'you' at work to the one you are at home and then again, a different 'you' with friends compared to with your family. And that's okay. We all have multiple sides to our personalities and there are some people who just understand certain traits we have more than others. It helps to have diversity in your friendships to reflect this because we all have more than one way of being.

Having authentic friendships that flow both ways is also important. You need to receive support as much as you need to give it. It can get really tiring when you are the one giving all the time, and it's pretty unfair if you're constantly taking from a friendship. Aim to have honest and balanced relationships where you feel you can be yourself. If you can't, then it's time to move on.

Being the most honest and true version of yourself as much as possible is the key. Are you living your beliefs? Do you truly believe in what you are doing? For example, if you are anti-gambling then taking a job at a casino would probably make you feel fairly uncomfortable. Seems obvious, right? This is known as cognitive dissonance. So, try and keep your choices consistent with your values. Sometimes those choices may not be the most popular decisions with your friends and family either, like choosing a job that pays less because it is more in line with your beliefs, but they will be authentic, which is what matters.

Life is grey, not black and white, and there will undoubtedly be times when you will need to bend. At work we may find that our professional and courteous self needs to show its face more often than not. Unfortunately, that is just part and parcel of working life. So, I bend . . . not so much that my moral compass is out of whack, but enough to get the job done. If I find that the bending is veering too close to breaking and stopping me from being able to be the real me, then I will make the move to another work environment that I feel is a better fit.

I feel calmer and more at peace within myself when I am being my true authentic self, and there is real beauty in that honesty.

be kind

when i asked a group of eleven-year-old girls what made someone beautiful, the first answer was not their hair, face, smile or clothes but how they acted – it was kindness.

I think kindness is so underrated. I'm always banging on about it because it would have to be my favourite human trait. It flows into so many areas of your life and it's not just about being kind to those around you – it's also about being kind to yourself.

We can be our own worst critics. In fact, I could probably list my bad bits endlessly. I look in the mirror and examine my well-travelled face and, like most women do with their own, I judge mine too harshly. I point out my flaws to anyone who will listen. I can't remember the last time I pointed out my good bits – probably because I could name them on one hand

the worried frown line between my eyebrows diminishes. I'm happier and that makes me feel more beautiful.

So, rather than scoff down the last biscuit on the plate, offer it to the person you are with first. If they don't want it, then eat away. Open the door for someone, help an older person with their bags. Look to see where you can make a difference. A kind word or gesture doesn't cost you very much but it means a lot to the person you are helping. It's thinking of others before yourself, it's being thoughtful.

and they are still just bits. So, I have to remind myself constantly to be kind to myself.

I find it easier to be kind to others. I like the feeling of giving. I think perhaps it's an especially female trait that we want those around us to feel good, but sometimes we do that at the expense of ourselves. When I am being kind to myself, I feel more accepting and less critical of how I look. Yes, I've got cellulite and flabby upper arms – but so what? I am what I am and that's okay.

Going to get a pedicure, having a long bath and even doing exercise are all ways that I show myself some extra kindness. Making the time for the skincare habits I talk about later in the book is an important part of self-care too (see page 64). It's about making me a priority. When I do that,

This flows through to thinking before you speak. If you take a minute to actually think about what you are going to say then a kinder word will possibly end up coming out of your mouth. You will say what you mean, not the first thought that has popped into your head. Give yourself the gift of taking your time with your words.

When I'm being kind to others it's not just in words or actions – it's also in the thoughts in my head. If someone is being a pain in the arse, rather than condemning them I will try to remember that I don't know what events have happened to them to make them behave in that way and, for all I know, they might need my kindness most of all.

be honourable

honesty is never on sale or for sale.

One of the quickest ways to destroy a relationship of any kind is to be untrustworthy. It is the opposite of being honourable, which extends into many areas. It's being honest and having integrity and strong moral principles. It's sticking to your word and being true to yourself. It's being a loyal and trustworthy friend. I'm certainly not Gandhi but I'm a long way from Lance Armstrong, too.

Behaving honourably means choosing the right thing, even when no-one else is looking. I remember standing in a supermarket next to the ATM where someone had obviously withdrawn money but somehow forgotten to take it – it was lying on the floor for some weird reason. Anyway, the supermarket was deserted and it was really, really tempting to just put that money in my pocket. But then I thought, what if that money belonged to a single mum who was withdrawing her last dollars for her sick kid? Aaah . . . so I took it to the help desk. (Amazingly enough, the supermarket ended up ringing me after a few months to come down and collect it as no-one had claimed it. What a little miracle!)

I need to be able to trust my friends and family. Trust is a building block of any relationship and if there is little or no trust then the foundation of that relationship is flawed from the beginning. That's a big problem because eventually, no matter how much you try, that relationship will show some serious cracks as a result.

We all know the people we can completely trust in our lives. These honourable people are as precious as diamonds. Most of us are also aware of our own levels of integrity and how flexible they may be. I want my friends and family to feel like they can depend on me – it's important that I keep my integrity intact despite the constant daily temptations that can reduce it to just a thin veneer. So, I'm painting a diamond coating around mine.

Sparkly, beautiful integrity that anyone can cultivate . . . and it won't cost you a cent.

be responsible

There is no point in accusing others for your own failings. Politicians are experts in blaming anyone within sight for their own shortcomings – any excuse will do. But when we take responsibility, we realise that we alone are accountable for our own choices in life. When you truly take charge of your life, then decisions you make are yours alone.

Being responsible is sometimes a hard thing to do. Life can get in the way. Having the clarity to look at yourself without excuses for your own behaviour is tricky, but it's a way that you can recognise and possibly alter your faults. Most of your friends are probably going to be reluctant to tell you your shortcomings, but hopefully you have one or two really close ones or a sibling who would be happy to fill you in from time to time (without taking too much pleasure in the criticism!).

At the end of the day, this is your life and you are responsible for your own choices. We are lucky to live in a society that values freedom and allows us to make our own decisions that ultimately may impact society for the better. When weighing up your options and thinking about the potential outcomes, try to think more broadly than yourself. Life is about we,

it all starts and ends with you.

not me. If we all thought of each other a little more then the world would be a better place, and how awesome would that be!

And if other people try to make you responsible for their problems, you need to have the strength to stand up for yourself – because who is going to defend you if you can't be bothered? Having an honest conversation with the person in question is usually the only answer. It takes balls to do that, and you may be amazed at the lack of communication that has caused the problem in the first place.

So, although it's not always easy, being responsible is worthwhile. It means that you're growing as a human being and that's beautiful. Simply by picking up this book you are taking responsibility for fulfilling your own potential and if you ask me that means you're already on your way to a richer and happier life.

be generous

I like giving. I like the feeling that it gives me inside. I'm not always generous though, especially if I am eating my favourite chocolates . . . you would have to wrestle me to the ground to get the melted choccy out of my death-like grip! But what I'm really talking about is being generous in spirit.

Generosity spills over into many areas: staying back after a party and helping clean up when you are exhausted, taking the time to sit and listen when your friends have problems. Generosity is not just when it suits you. It's about making yourself available when it suits others.

Listening is one of the most generous acts you can do. People want to share their thoughts – it helps with feeling connected and better about the world. You don't need to offer an opinion, you can just be a sounding board. Women vent all the time and often we actually don't need a solution, we just want to be heard – though sometimes we solve our own problems simply through being given the space to let it all out.

We've all been guilty of being less than generous with our emotional support. I can remember a few times when I really didn't get the message – because it wasn't important to me – until I turned around and

we make a living by what we get but a life by what we give.

My partner's father passed away a couple of years ago. It was sudden and unexpected – he was the healthiest grandparent around, bicycling over 200 km a week – but he had a massive heart attack and boom. Dead instantaneously in the backyard daffodil patch. He'd always complained about being broke and it was his reason for not doing most things or not helping his kids out when they truly needed it.

It came time to clean out his home and while my partner and his relatives were emptying it, they found a massive amount of cash stuffed in various places around the house: in the oven, under the sink, in a safe that didn't lock and even up in the roof. It was bittersweet because they ended up with it all, yet they felt deeply disappointed in their father.

Be generous when you have the chance. It adds to your life.

saw my friend in tears. I actually said to her, 'Are you joking, or is this for real?' Yep, sometimes I just need a sledgehammer over the head.

My closest friend has been on the listening end of many tears and frustrations. She has patiently listened to me cry over doomed relationships, injustices and my own personal failings. I know I can be completely vulnerable with her and not be judged for it. Sometimes I get a little bit of 'Snap out of it', sometimes laughter and sometimes I just get compassionate listening. Whatever it is, it's what I need at the time because she knows me so well.

be grateful

There is so much to be grateful for. I'm lucky I'm in good health. I appreciate the good friendships that I have. I look for beauty in the world. It can be anywhere. It's in the garden on a sunny morning. It's in the rainbows on a rainy day. It's in everyday occurrences like being brought a cup of tea in bed – heaven!

I try to appreciate everything that I have and am. This can certainly be tricky when we are constantly comparing ourselves to others and what they may or may not have. It's a natural instinct for us. It's called social comparison theory and it's a way in which we measure our own success. We compare our looks, status, wealth and intelligence plus many other little traits with those of others to establish our own worth. But in the past decade we've been given numerous apps like Facebook and Instagram that almost make comparison a sport . . . it's a more than daily occurrence.

The world-famous businessman Warren Buffett has said that the world is driven not by greed, but by envy – and I think there is much truth to that statement. There are positives that come out of comparing, though. It can drive us to strive to be more like someone we admire. It can also remind us to feel more appreciative of our own circumstances when we see someone who we consider less fortunate than us. In general, I try to run my own race because I feel that looking at where others are going is really not that relevant to me. I have my own journey. I am not them and they are not me. But yep, I still compare – everyone does.

Then there's the frustrating thing that we're all guilty of: moving the goalposts whenever we accomplish a goal. Rather than being content with the achievement, we say 'Now I want . . . ' This can be inspirational but remember to appreciate and celebrate your victories as well. Take a moment to be grateful that you have made it to where you wanted to go before you go charging off on your next mission.

When I walk to school with my daughter I am always pointing out the beauty around us. We stop and smell beautiful flowers and sometimes sit in the morning sun having a drink. I will sit quietly and stare at her beautiful face, until she tells me to stop. We take the time to appreciate the beauty that is everywhere. We also keep a gratitude journal and make it a habit to say what the best part of our day was over dinner, to help us remember the need to be grateful for what we have.

'everything has beauty but not everyone sees it.' – confucius

be brave

we all need to be brave in order to get the absolute most out of our lives.

When I think of bravery I initially think of knights going into battle. Fighting without fear of the outcome – or possibly having that fear and doing it anyway.

I remember when I was younger there was a beauty competition at the local department store and even though it was in the children's department I still qualified because I was under fourteen. I desperately wanted the clothing voucher, so I entered. I didn't have aspirations to be a model so I was putting myself way out of my comfort zone.

As I was larger than most of the other 'children' participating they needed to take me to the womenswear department to dress me. I was quickly put into bright blue skintight pants and a yellow flowing top. I was then asked to dance my way down the catwalk amongst the other 'children', most of whom barely came up to my waist. So humiliating! And to top it all off, when I looked out into the audience

I could see my school-teacher standing there watching me – aaah. It did have a good outcome when I won the second-prize clothing voucher, plus I realised that I actually enjoyed the process of dressing up and my fragile teenage confidence had increased. Success!

Be brave when it comes to relationships. Approach potential partners and let them know you're interested, be open to finding love. It's not embarrassing – it's fearless. Men and women aren't psychic, sometimes people need a nudge. Internet dating is great for that, but nothing can beat a one-on-one conversation. It's so much more personal. Bravery is needed at the end of a relationship, too – it's hard to move forward if you've got your head stuck in the past.

Be brave at work. Put up your hand for a promotion. Let people know you're there and that you can contribute. Say no when you need to. Move on if you have to. Think outside the box sometimes. You're valuable and have worth – so let other people know it too. If you've made a mistake put your hand up, be accountable – we all make mistakes and others respect that.

Be brave in life. Try new adventures, travel to different countries. It will open up the way you see the world and that makes you a more accepting person. Trying new sports or clothing or looks are all different ways of being brave. We are all so much braver than we truly imagine and if we can just tap into that then the rewards are so great they make any temporary discomfort or fear worth it.

put yourself out of your comfort zone.

be light-hearted

'do not take life
too seriously.
you will never
get out of it alive.'
– elbert hubbard

I work with a gorgeous girl who is blonde, cute and sexy . . . but that is not solely what makes her so attractive. She is just so incredibly funny and keeps me laughing on set all day. I look forward to those work days. To me, she is so much more attractive than many of the models we work with because she is smart and funny. It's a lethal combo, in my book.

I absolutely love a great sense of humour. I feel so relaxed after having a big laugh and it is a beauty trait that is truly transformative. Picture Robin Williams for a minute – he was not classically handsome by any means but he was hysterically funny, and that made him so very attractive to men and women. It's all about timing and intelligence. It takes brainpower to be funny. I just love people who can laugh at themselves and don't take life too seriously.

Just take a look at kids: they are always laughing. I find it really refreshing to spend time with them, looking at the silly side of life. Sit down and watch a kids' movie with them – humour often plays a starring role. Jump on a trampoline and just try to keep the smile off your face! Make a conscious decision to add more laughter and smiles into your life by putting up reminders of happy times like photos. Change your screensaver to a picture of a time when you had a great laugh. These little changes will all help keep a smile on your dial.

There have been many times throughout my life when things just seem so bad that they absolutely can't get any worse . . . and then wham: another crappy thing hits home. Often at that point my disbelief turns to laughter – I find they sit close together on the emotional scale. So when things aren't great I prefer to laugh than get upset. It makes me feel better and I know it absolutely makes me look better when I am happier.

Humour is lovable and memorable. It sends out a signal that you are easy to talk to and approachable. Laughing may make you appear more beautiful and attractive too. I find it makes people appear younger. A big laugh also releases endorphins into your body that make you feel good and release tension – it's basic biology. So laugh away . . .

be passionate

When we really love doing something our whole faces light up. We feel inspired and driven by the sheer joy of participating in something that means something to us. We lose track of time and are engrossed in the act, like when I'm giving someone a makeover – I can't get enough.

When we follow our passion, it feels like we're on the right path and things just seem to flow smoothly. Everyone is unique, we all have different roads to travel, so what you feel passionate about is going to be different to me. But what we both have in common is how happy we feel when taking part in our chosen passion.

There is no defining time to develop a passion – I believe we can have them from age two to ninety-two. They will possibly change from collecting stuffed teddies to collecting china as they evolve throughout our lives, but that's one of the great things about life: we change. Not always to suit others, but hopefully to better ourselves.

I took up sculpture a couple of years ago and I'm obsessed. I am in love with clay and anything to do with it. I will sit for hours with art books or sculpt until my hands hurt, and I spent hours in the Musée Rodin in Paris soaking up all of the amazing sculptures. It's a passion and a somewhat new and surprising one.

i am passionate about beauty: the inside, the outside, the fleeting and the forever.

It's attractive to see someone passionate. To hear someone talk knowledgeably about their chosen subject is interesting. They make it interesting because they have such love for it. So, if you are unsure where your passions lie, then take a look at what you are naturally good at and what you are interested in because they may be lying in plain sight waiting for you to discover them.

be accepting

The world is made up of more people than male and female, straight and gay – there are a whole host of other people who don't fit into traditional stereotypes. If we could all just get over our obsession with putting a 'label' on everyone then that would be really fantastic and a great start. At the end of the day we are all just people – simple.

Let's embrace and accept everyone. That includes yourself. If you have super cute freckles on your face, show them. You don't need heavy foundation to cover what is unique to you. Change your perception: those freckles are an asset. If you have beautiful porcelain skin then embrace it,

get rid of the fake tanning. I have a friend who has been battling her pale skin for years – she's been spending time and money trying to join up the dots (or freckles) for a tan for about ten years . . . and nope, it doesn't work.

Let's face it, as we age our bodies change and not always in ways we want. We freak out when we start to get boobs in our early teens and then freak out again when our stomachs don't magically spring back after having a baby. Our expectations of ourselves are so high and we really need to cut ourselves some slack. No-one is looking at you with the same critical eye

our looks are just our packaging, and we are all wrapped differently.

that you have, and you would never talk to your best friend with the same scorn with which you talk to yourself. Remember, no-one is perfect. Life is a journey and we are all going to have good and bad days, but if we can try to enjoy the roller-coaster ride of life rather than agonising over every change it will make the ride so much more rewarding.

When we were young we wanted to be older, when we got to be teenagers we lied and made ourselves look older to get into bars and clubs, then when we had children we started turning the clock back. We feared being too old. But what age is 'too old', and too old for what, anyway? Should

I start lying now? Maybe I should have started twenty years ago . . . LOL. Funnily enough my mum, who is in her eighties, tells me her friends wear their age like a badge of honour. I like that. So let's make it perfectly fine to be the age we are . . . what a relief that would be.

On the inside we don't differ that much at all: we all have a heart and blood and bones. Where we do differ is in our external looks and our beliefs. Unfortunately, those beliefs become problematic if we are not tolerant of others with differing points of view. And since tolerance can be in short supply in this world, we need to look to ourselves first. It's like a house of cards: if I can be tolerant, then maybe my friends can and their friends can . . . and hopefully it spreads from there like a Mexican wave. It doesn't matter what colour your skin or language you speak; we are all fundamentally the same.

At the end of the day, we are all going through our own life journey and if we can make it as exciting and meaningful as possible for ourselves and the other lives we touch then I think we have done okay. So open up your arms and embrace this huge, messy, huggable world. It's a beautiful place!

be respectful

There is an extremely long tradition of respect in Japan. It is essential to have flawless manners and to behave in a certain way. When we had our first of many Japanese exchange students come to stay with us, it became abundantly clear who had the best manners – and it wasn't us! Owi would bend at the waist when saying goodnight. She would write little thankyou notes when we took her out for the day and even went to my daughter's school to teach them origami – it was lovely. We felt very valued because of her respectfulness.

I like good manners. Yes, I may sometimes swear like a f***ing lunatic, but I always remember to thank people for services they have done for me. I feel this is especially important with waitresses, cleaners or anyone else in the service industry. I'm essentially acknowledging their work and that's important. I try to teach my daughter this and it must have stuck because her kindergarten teacher said she had the best manners in her entire class. Awesome – I did something right!

Respecting yourself involves treating your body with the care it deserves. That doesn't mean you're a princess, it just means that you think twice before you put substances, excessive alcohol or people into it that

a few modern-day tips for being respectful:

- Don't look at your phone when having a conversation with someone – be fully present
- Be on time to meetings or social engagements
- Answer your texts and emails in a timely manner (not three days later)
- Accept others' points of view with grace, regardless of whether you agree or not
- If you say you're going to do something, do it
- Be appreciative of others
- Be humble and aware of others' circumstances

possibly don't belong. It's essential to respect yourself first because if you don't care about yourself, how can you expect others to?

My daughter's piano teacher, Madeline, is only tiny, but commands respect. She is self-confident, polite and speaks with conviction. She is honest, kind, open and a good listener. She dresses well, plus she's authentic and smart. I think that's amazing for someone who's only twenty-two years old. If someone told me she will be prime minister in twenty years I'd nod my head and agree. I'd vote for her! I believe that you need to earn respect, just like a carefully

tended garden or a clean house. It doesn't magically happen, it takes work to get it and it takes thought to show it. But to see it is a thing of beauty.

respect begins and ends with yourself.

be curious

Being good-looking sure as sh*t does not make you beautiful. I've met many a pretty face that was only that: pretty on the outside. It's a vacuous way to be and one that no-one should aspire to. I can think of countless people who are famous for their looks and not much else, and I know many people ask the same thing that I'm thinking: is that it?

Brainpower is sexy. Adding to conversations and having a well-informed view of the world makes you a more interesting and attractive person. Possibly you've been through university or done some sort of extended learning and that's great, but there are many ways of expanding your mind.

Podcasts, reading and documentaries are all avenues to increase your knowledge. I listen to podcasts while I am out walking as they are an invaluable means to learn other people's points of view. It gives me a new perspective on the world – something I never used to care about has suddenly become very interesting.

Keeping an open mind may also make your life easier. There are so many new technologies on the market: apps to make your life flow smoothly and gadgets

'i have no special talents. i am only passionately curious.'
– albert einstein

to enhance your experiences. These all require new learning and some are easier than others, but even if I am finding it hard to learn something new, like how to program our ridiculously complicated TV set, I will persevere with it. I always take an information headset when at the art gallery. It completely changes the way I look at art and adds to the experience because really taking the time to look at what's around you can totally change how you relate to it.

The flip side of this is that you do need to be sceptical sometimes, too. It's very easy to be influenced in our day-to-day lives by people, news and companies. In 1938, *Time* magazine made Adolf Hitler 'Man of

the Year', even putting him on the cover – can you believe it? And in the '20s there was a soap called La-Mar that promised to wash away body fat and make you look younger – amazing claims from a completely sudsy product. You're not a sheep, so think for yourself and resist the temptation to put your brain in park. Just because everyone else is doing it, that doesn't mean it's right. Be sceptical about what is presented to you as the truth. At the end of the day you need to make up your own mind and think for yourself.

There are many claims made by beauty products today that are pretty outrageous, like making you look ten years younger in twenty days or erasing fine lines or plumping up lips. Don't you think that if there was a truly magical product like that out there then we would all already know about it? Spoiler alert: some products might help, but there are no magic fixes.

So keep a curious mind. If you haven't given your brain a workout lately, take a look around to see what you may be interested in and dip your toe into the pond of knowledge. It can only add to your intelligence and that's a thing of beauty. Pretty and smart: a potent combination and something to aspire to.

be confident

I've been making up faces – famous and not so famous – for years. I can see the uncertainty and self-criticism in a woman's eye when she looks in the mirror before she gets 'worked on'. It doesn't matter if you sit on multiple boards or if your claim to fame is your voice: we're all the same in the bathroom mirror. The insecurities slowly disappear as the makeup mask goes on. Many of the most beautiful faces I have worked on have the lowest self-esteem. It's so ironic. They will pick themselves to pieces in the mirror.

We are bombarded with images of how we are supposed to look. It usually includes a ton of grooming and sometimes takes a ton of money to achieve. It's not realistic and everyone who works in fashion knows it. We know it's impossible to look like that – in fact, even the models who are in the photos often say that they don't look like that. It takes retouching, time and money to create those unrealistic images. No wonder we can never feel like we're good enough when we make constant comparisons against something that no-one can achieve.

Does your confidence rely on the clothes you wear and the makeup and hairstyle you have? Clearly for many of us it does, and

**many small
victories = big
confidence**

that's why I've included outer beauty tips and tricks in the second half of this book – I know I certainly feel more confident if I am having a good hair and makeup day topped off with a great outfit, though I don't have the time or energy to do that every day. But I really don't want my total confidence relying too heavily on how I look. We are all so much more than that. What is more important to my confidence is my inner strengths, so I remind myself of them often. I take care of my exterior but it is not the only good thing about me.

I try to remember that I can look just as good wearing jeans and a t-shirt with next to no makeup on. I honestly believe that this is true of most women but we get so used to seeing ourselves with a face full of makeup that it becomes a layer of protection. I believe finding self-confidence is simply a matter of attitude, and French women seem to have it mastered – they ooze confidence out of their very chic pores. There are many small signals that tell us that a woman is confident. It's a strong walk, a purposeful way of speaking, maintaining eye contact. There is a certain nonchalance to wearing an outfit. She doesn't fidget. She is a good listener. She doesn't blame others. Real self-assurance doesn't involve staring in

tell yourself repeatedly, 'I am enough' – and believe it because you are.

a simple way to increase your own confidence is to change the negative messages in your head to positive ones. put sticky notes on your mirror with positive reinforcements written on them, or just say them to yourself in the shower, or even get them printed on a t-shirt for the whole world to see. here are a few that I like:

i am enough

i look hot

i'm not only gorgeous but i'm kind

i'm just as smart as everyone else

i have worth

i am stronger than i think

i can do it

– and finally, but most importantly –

i love me.

the mirror and it doesn't involve a ton of makeup: it's a security from within yourself.

No-one can give you confidence, you need to grow it for yourself. It comes with time and experience slowly building up. It's about loving yourself for what and who you are and celebrating that every day. Confidence means you are running your own race – you're not comparing or competing, you're just doing. You get it from approaching life from a fearless perspective. It's having the courage within yourself to say no when you're really a people pleaser. It's being strong in your beliefs.

be optimistic

I absolutely love being around people who are optimistic. I want the glass to be half full not half empty – it simply makes me feel better being that way and I prefer to be around people who share the same attitude. I find them more attractive and – no surprise – they also live longer according to many medical studies.

Optimism can be learnt, so every time you hear a little negative remark in your head question it straight away. Take a good listen to what you are saying to yourself – you will probably find that when you tune in calmly to what you're hearing, much of your internal dialogue is fear-based. If you can get past that fear and dare to dream then you'll be able to lead the best life that you can.

An optimist looks at problems as a challenge and doesn't take failure as the final answer – there is usually always another way. They aren't afraid to try. They figure, 'Why not? Give it a go.' Go on a blind date? Give it a go. Try Vietnamese food? Give it a go. Climb Mount Everest? Give it a go. It's a powerful and liberating way to be. Sometimes people think too long and hard about actually doing something or even anything. I say just do it. Don't wait. Time is all we've got. Nothing is guaranteed in life, neither success nor failure, so what are you waiting for?

i like 'i can'
– not 'i can't'.

I remember I was in Bali on a boat in the middle of the ocean, no land in sight. We saw a pod of dolphins in the water and thought, let's jump in, why not. So we did – without over-thinking – and it was amazing! The bluest, deepest water I have ever seen, dolphins swimming past . . . magical. That image is embedded in my memory. If I'd stopped and thought about how far the jump was and maybe getting eaten by sharks and how I was ever going to get back on the boat and . . . I would never have done it. There is a beauty and excitement in the unknown. Sometimes we need to jump.

We all need to have hope that our future will be great. We hoped for little things when we were kids, like getting a Barbie for Christmas or that our mums would take us for ice-cream after a hot day at school. There was the hope my daughter nervously voiced on her first day of kinder: that she would make friends. Simple and heartfelt hopes and dreams.

Eventually life gets busy and noisy and our hopes may start to wane. Don't give up. Let's all be optimistic that the world will be a better place. If we act on that hope then it is no longer a dream but a revolution. I hope for my daughter's future and I am going to make darn sure that I do my best to make that hope a reality. I will put in place everything I can to achieve the best outcome.

I plan on rolling with the punches, because undoubtedly life is going to throw those at us, but I am going to hang on to my optimism with all my might. I know there will be times when I feel like giving up on hope, so I try to wait out the storm. I rest, I don't surrender. When I am feeling stronger I pick my hope back up and go along my merry way. No-one is going to take that hope away from me. It's mine.

be genuinely connected

Social media can be the biggest show-off platform there is. It's 24/7 as well. I get tired of looking at touched-up selfies – it doesn't feel real. I want substance and I think that a lot of us feel the same way. Many of the models I work with say just that, and an increasing number of them are giving social media a break. For some it's a complete split but for others it's just a break for a week or two.

Isn't it weird that we talk about an app on our phones as if it's a relationship? Like any relationship, if you're not getting as much out of it as you're putting in, then leave. Luckily this breakup can be done with one finger and no tears. Treat Facebook, Instagram and other social platforms with the casual disdain that they really deserve. Occasionally throw them a crumb but keep

your distance . . . and whatever you do, don't get sucked in or you'll end up with a stage five clinger.

Most social media apps are run off algorithms and personalise your content so that you want to watch more. So, if you've recently been liking, say, llamas dressed in pink fluffy jumpers, it's no accident that suddenly there are more of them on your feed. What we see in these mini online worlds is not a reflection of accurately portrayed real life and we need to remember that. Yes, it can be good to stay connected, but if you find yourself wasting big chunks of your day on it then you may have a problem.

It truly doesn't matter how many followers or 'friends' you have. I like to actually know what my 'friends' look like! I notice when I travel on the train that everyone has their head stuck in their phone looking at their social media when they could be talking to their real friend who may be sitting right next to them. Newsflash: you're missing an opportunity to really connect. Or maybe I should run that line in bold across your feed so you get the message . . .

Loneliness is now a growing health epidemic, particularly in wealthy countries that have wholeheartedly embraced social media. Initially we all thought it was such a fun thing to help us keep in contact with our friends but, over time, it seems to have turned into a monster. It consumes every waking minute, making us feel lonelier than ever. We really need to keep it in perspective. Life is a dialogue, not a monologue – and I don't know about you, but I get sick of talking about myself very quickly.

At the end of the day, it's great to have genuine real-life and social media connections with a whole range of friends. Spending time with them in person is a beautiful part of life that will create memories and experiences that you can cherish for the rest of your life. That's the important stuff. We just need to remember it.

i like to know what my real friends look like.

be open

I had a part-time job during high school as a checkout chick at the local discount department store. I eventually got promoted to the 'help desk' (cigarette-selling booth) where I was in my element: the booth was situated right next to the ladies' fashion department and change rooms. Yippee!

I would spend my time 'making over' willing and not-so-willing customers, persuading them to try on many different ensembles and then urgently paging my work mates on the loudspeaker to come and give their approval in oohs and aahs. It was great – I loved creating the transformation and the customers loved the encouragement from enthusiastic teenagers. I could see the confidence and happiness in their eyes when they felt beautiful. It would almost always end in a sale – not that I cared if they bought anything, though. I just wanted them to feel good.

Fashion is about fun, and that extends to makeup and hair. So, don't be slow to get a new haircut or try something new in makeup – a new lipstick colour, a different eyeshadow. It's meant to be short-term. It's meant to be experimental. Join in. When the holidays come at the end of every year my daughter and I put a colour rinse into our hair – last year she had purple, the year before I went for pink. It's a way we

celebrate the holiday season. It makes me feel fresh, plus it also gives us a bit of swagger in our attitude! It's amazing what a bit of colour can do.

I find that as we get older we can be less daring in our beauty choices. We think we know what 'suits us' but hey, here's a news flash: there are more hairstyles than a bob that are going to look great and there are more styles of makeup than 'natural' that are going to suit you.

I know how much we can be influenced by our friends and family that are used to the 'old' us, but give yourself that permission to embrace change. I find that if I am open

to change it makes my life more interesting. I enjoy looking at life from a new short-haired point of view. I go in with the attitude of, 'Why not?'. Choose a new hairdresser who looks at you with a different eye, wear a colour that's unfamiliar to you. Hair will grow back, makeup can be washed off and clothes can be changed, but if you never try you'll never know.

If you're open to the power of transformation and you believe, then you can make anything work.

be mindful

truly listen
to yourself.

Many years ago, I used to travel to Munich to do fashion makeup work. I had an über efficient agent there called Katya and she was a machine. Not long after arriving in Germany, I'd be off doing go-sees where I would meet potential employers to introduce myself and generally rave on about how fabulous I was – LOL. The idea was that if they liked me, they would book me on some of their photo shoots throughout Europe. After the go-sees were completed I would have to wait. Sometimes the waiting didn't take long but other times it could take weeks to get a booking.

In the meantime, I would ride my bike around Munich, walk in the massive city park across the road from my apartment or read. It was a solitary and quiet time. I could go the entire day without speaking to anyone (except for the corner bakery fraulein who served me my breakfast of Brezel und Kaffee and seemed to understand my Scheiße [crap] German).

What I found from the enforced speaking retreat was that a serenity and peace would descend upon me. Initially that voice in my head would still be talking at 10 000 frantic miles an hour but eventually,

because I gave it so much time to chat undisturbed, it would slow down to an easy conversation that I was able to focus on. I could really hear and feel what was going on within myself. I was able to be mindful and present much more easily. Yoga and meditation are great ways to achieve the same state, but even simple things like taking a solo walk or slowly and carefully washing the dishes can help you tune back in to yourself.

Occasionally I'll deliberately give myself some 'blue sky time', which means that I am not hooked up to any kind of media.

I am just sitting or lying down, allowing my mind to wander at will. Holidays are a great time for this – my mind becomes clear, which helps me with making big decisions. I can really connect to my inner voice and ultimately decide what it is that I want out of life. It's big-picture stuff and it's important for all of us.

If the voice in your head has to yell for you to hear it or is constantly throwing a tantrum for your attention, maybe it's time to stop and listen. After all, the most important person to listen to is yourself.

be humble

Someone who has humility does not believe they are better than others. In this age of competition that can be challenging – it's difficult not to compare ourselves. I do it too often and am forever reminding myself to run my own race. In other words, I am only competing against myself. When I want to compare, I try to look back on my earlier life then make the comparison between now and then. There is no point in comparing with someone else – that's their life, it's not mine.

I recently worked on an international hair competition with a veteran hairdresser, Wendy. She is in her sixties but doesn't look a day over fifty in her leather pants and fuchsia lipstick. She made it to the finals of the comp, so I went along to do her models' makeup. When we had finished with her Tibetan model, who was standing there with her newly coloured apricot-and-pink hair, we all took a minute to look around. We noticed that most of the other finalists were in their twenties and thirties. Wendy had been so busy running her own race, she could have been the only person in the room rather than one of sixty standing amongst noisy hairdryers and excited chatter. And she ended up winning the entire competition.

> '**humility, that low, sweet root, from which all heavenly virtues shoot.'
> – thomas moore**

Being humble doesn't mean you disregard compliments; it means accepting them graciously. I used to have a problem with that. Every time someone would compliment me I'd say, 'No I'm not.' You're pretty . . . no I'm not. You're funny . . . no I'm not. I only realised how offensive that was to the person giving the compliment when a few people said that same remark back to me. Now I accept the positive remark with a smile and say a modest thank you. Simple.

Humility is expressed not only in the words you say but also in the actions you take. If you truly believe that you are no better in the world than anyone else then your actions will reflect that. You will treat all races and classes the same. It is a way of living and believing.

But there is a difference between being humble and being a doormat. A doormat gets walked over and a humble person gets walked beside. I like to walk beside people – I don't need their shoe marks on my back. If you find you have scuff marks on your back, get up off the floor – you don't belong there.

be in tune with nature

our earth is beautiful and precious.

Get out into nature. It will make you feel better. If you've had a stressful day or week, go and find some greenery – leave the city if you can or just get out into a park. Being in and surrounded by nature has the potential to reduce your stress levels, blood pressure and heart rate. It may give you a well-needed boost and an increased sense of wellbeing. It's great for your body and mind.

Make more meaningful choices as a consumer to simplify and declutter your life and help protect the future of our planet. If we all start acting with intent then the next thing we know, meaningful change will be just around the corner – and that makes the world a better place for everyone.

The earth is only getting more densely inhabited, with global population increasing every year. I try to be mindful about the impact my life has for future generations and if that means buying fewer clothes and looking a little more carefully at my consumer choices, then I think that is an easy enough thing for me or anyone else to do for such an important cause.

Fashion has become so fast and many of us consume, consume, consume. Before you go shopping ask yourself if you really need whatever it is you're heading out to buy, or whether you're actually just looking for a shopping fix. I know it's a hard question for many of us who love to shop! Did you know that the self-storage industry is booming? In Australia its revenue is now around $1 billion per year. If we can't fit all this stuff in our homes then that's a problem. Clearly we don't really need it if we are just going to store it elsewhere!

Recycle your clothing. I also shop in op shops and at vintage markets – I have bought many an amazing jacket there and I get so excited when I score a bargain. Notice where your clothing and beauty products are made, too, to help you choose with discretion. I don't want four-year-olds in India or China making my clothing. I don't think any of us do. I value my clothing more if it is ethically made.

All my seemingly minor everyday decisions about purchases have a knock-on effect – it's a very small way in which I can contribute to a healthier earth. If we all became more conscious about our individual impact on the environment and society – along with price and quality – we'd make very different and more positive choices.

Being environmentally responsible will make you a better person. And I believe a better person is a more beautiful one.

beautiful habits

a habit is something that you do often and regularly, sometimes without really knowing that you are doing it.

by building daily beauty habits into your routine, you are investing in yourself and, like the interest on your savings account, a little amount each day really adds up over time.

seven simple habits for beautiful skin

1. **wear sunscreen** prevent sun damage (page 66)
2. **be hydrated** drink water (page 70)
3. **get a good night's sleep** be fresh and revitalised (page 72)
4. **be fit** exercise to get the blood pumping and oxygenate your skin (page 74)
5. **be relaxed** minimise stress, take a break (page 76)
6. **be nutritious** build a diet of fresh, whole foods with lots of greens and amino acids (page 78)
7. **look after your gut** boost its health with prebiotics and probiotics (page 80)

One of the questions I'm asked most often is what people can do to improve their skin – it's something we all want. I'll touch on each of these points in more detail later on, but here's the lowdown on what you really need to do if you want healthy, smooth, glowing skin. The great thing is that many of these habits don't cost anything and lots of them have extra benefits for your body and mind too – it's a win–win!

Beautiful, healthy and glowing skin can be yours by simply following these seven habits. Make them a part of your daily routine and watch your skin improve day by day. They will do so much more than an expensive moisturiser or face cream. Funnily enough, beauty often works from the inside out. Think about how fantastic you look after coming back from holidays – you've probably been doing many of these habits while away. So, why not make them a part of your everyday life and look amazing seven days a week?

habit #1

wear sunscreen

this is probably the most important tip that i can give you for maintaining beautiful skin.

The sun can be brutal, so put on a sunscreen every day. Australians have one of the highest skin cancer rates in the world and are particularly at risk due to our proximity to the ozone hole over the Antarctic, which means that our UV exposure is especially high. The shape of the earth's orbit also brings this part of the earth closer to the sun during summer. Most of the damage done to our skin is from the sun, so protect yourself 365 days a year – not just when you're on holiday. And it doesn't matter if it's cloudy; you still need to wear it.

There are two types of UV light that you need to worry about: UVA and UVB. You need to buy a sunscreen with a broad-spectrum coverage to protect you from both, and it should be minimum SPF 15 but ideally SPF 50 for your face, neck and upper chest (and other areas that are regularly exposed). It's best to apply it twenty minutes before you get into the sun. UV rays cause more than 80 per cent of the visible signs of ageing, which include wrinkles, rough patches, skin discolouration, spotting and sagging. So make sure you slap it on every day, reapplying every two hours; and top it with makeup that contains an SPF too. Combine the sunscreen with wearing a hat, sunglasses and protective clothing, plus of course standing in the shade when possible.

While you need to be mindful of sun damage, however, you don't want to end up with a vitamin D deficiency. This is a big problem in Australia, affecting about a third of the population. In order to get your daily dose of vitamin D, your actual skin needs to be directly exposed to the sun, so no sunscreen or shade and fewer clothes on low-UV days. According to the Cancer Council of Australia, for many of us, adequate vitamin D levels are reached through regular incidental exposure to the sun. When the UV index is high, such as during summer in the southern areas of Australia or all year round in the northern parts of the country, most people maintain adequate vitamin D levels just by spending a few minutes outdoors every day. During autumn and winter in the southern areas of Australia, when there is less sun, you will need to expose a bit of skin and spend a bit more time uncovered outdoors. In the northern parts of Australia, the UV levels are above 3 all year round during the day but it is safe to go outside without sun protection in the early morning and late afternoon when they're lower.

Vitamin D can also be obtained through your diet. Foods that contain vitamin D include fatty fish like salmon, trout and tuna, fish oils, cheese (eaten in moderation)

and egg yolks, as well as some fortified cereals and mushrooms that have been exposed to the sun.

When I was a teen, we used to slather our bodies in oil that had absolutely no SPF and then bake our bodies in the backyard until we either couldn't stand the heat or got burnt. I cringe to think of it now. We were a bit like rotisserie chickens, turning over every fifteen minutes. I remember one year, I got so fried that I had second-degree burns – my legs puffed up like two tight pink sausages! I was covered in blisters and man was it painful. I swore I would never bake again. Luckily, I don't

have to because there are much safer and healthier alternatives for getting a glow.

If you want to look more tanned the smart way, go to page 142 and I'll tell you the best methods how.

habit #2

be hydrated

a raisin is just a
grape without
the water.

Picture a raisin for a minute: all dried up and wrinkled. Now, picture a beautiful juicy grape: smooth and round and yummy. We all need to keep ourselves hydrated – and I want to be a grape, not a raisin! Our bodies are made up of approximately 60 per cent water and we need it to function properly. It's essential.

I try to drink at least eight glasses of water a day, more in summer or if I am exercising or sweating lots. Signs that you may not be getting enough water include urine that's darker than usual, constipation, headaches and dry skin. If you're thirsty, this is your body's natural, inbuilt signal for you to drink more. Carrying a water bottle around with you is a good idea, as it reminds you to drink up and means that you can spread out your water consumption across the day – our bodies can only absorb so much water at once before sending us running to the bathroom. Put a glass next to every meal as well, to remind yourself. It's easy to forget to drink – we've all been guilty of that. But think of water as your calorie-free friend who not only helps keep you healthy on the inside, but beautiful on the outside too.

The skin is 30 per cent water, and this water content contributes to its resilience, plumpness and elasticity. Yep, as far as H_2O is concerned, there's basically no bad news for our beautiful skin.

Don't only drink water – bathe in it, too. A calming bath releases stress and increases a feeling of wellbeing. When I remember, I place oils in my bath – they help with the feeling of serenity and make me feel good. Some of my favourites are lavender and chamomile to relax, bergamot to revitalise and eucalyptus if I have a cold. I also love going to natural springs and the beach – I feel the minerals in the water give me vitality.

When washing my face and body with water, I use a temperature that is comfortable: not too hot and not too cold. Too hot and my natural oils get washed down the sink; too cold and it may disrupt my capillaries, causing red blotchy skin. I want my skin to feel the gentle wash of warm water. But we all have our own different preferences for what suits us and what is comfortable in terms of temperature.

water in all its forms is one of life's miracles.

habit #3

get a good night's sleep

Sleep is the time that your body repairs itself: it's repairing damaged cells and producing collagen. Collagen acts like a fine net for your skin and helps to keep it looking firm. Studies on sleep suggest it's really important for our ability to metabolise glucose, and when we don't get enough sleep it can disrupt the function of the hormones that relate to appetite. And that's just for your body; it has a whole host of benefits for your mind, too. It's truly a restorative time.

If you've ever done much international flying, you will know that unless you're flying business or first class it is next to impossible to get a good night's sleep on a plane without drugging yourself up. I've often caught sight of my sleep-deprived face in the toilet mirror and I can see exactly why it's called 'beauty sleep': dark circles, blotchiness and no glow. Lack of sleep ages me very quickly. According to a small study carried out in Sweden, sleep-deprived people appear less healthy and less attractive. No shit, Sherlock!

If I haven't had a good night's sleep, it is almost guaranteed that I will be hunting through my cupboards the next day for a 'quick fix' – chocolate or something sweet – which I truly do not want to do. I am more

it's called 'beauty sleep' for a reason.

likely to make poorer choices for my body when I'm tired. Plus, I am really cranky to be around – not pleasant, and definitely not pretty!

Try to make your bedroom a little sanctuary of peace. Fresh bed linen, soft lighting and a clean body all help me to get a good night's rest. My beauty ritual at night consists of cleaning my face, teeth and body and then applying an organic rosehip oil to my face and massaging it in. Rosehip oil classifies as a dry oil, so it doesn't feel greasy on my face. I've also been known to head down to the kitchen and scoop out some of my organic coconut oil then rub

that on my face before bed . . . though I only do that if my skin is feeling dry or if I've had a day in the sun. (For more on oils, see page 90.)

If you can, try not to sleep with the air conditioner or heater blasting as these are both forms of dry air and they will dry out your skin. I find it best to sleep in a slightly cool room if possible.

I aim for nine hours of sleep a night, but I know that's not possible all the time or even any of the time for some people. Life just gets in the way. So, do your best and aim for a minimum of seven.

habit #4

be fit

physically and mentally.

I like to exercise – not so much that I am dying and can hardly breathe, but just enough so that I feel alive and energetic. It increases the oxygen that goes to my skin and that gives me a great glow. Sweating helps clean out my pores, as the trapped dirt and oil moves out with the sweat, cleansing my skin in the process. It's like getting a mini facial!

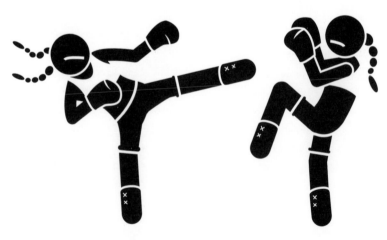

Obviously, being fit helps with keeping our weight under control, plus I find it keeps lethargy at bay. Exercise has also been proven to reduce cholesterol and improve cardiovascular fitness – so it's really important, as you can see. But while I know that regular exercise is great for my skin and helps with muscle tone, more than anything, I do it to make myself feel better mentally. I keep it enjoyable so that I look forward to it and don't feel it's a chore.

It's been proven that regular exercise can lower stress levels and improve mood, and it also helps with getting a great night's sleep (that is, if you're not having sex – because it can do your sex drive a few favours, too!).

I don't do the extreme 'get a bikini body in seven days' forms of exercise; I do the more long-term commitment, like moving my body for 10 000 steps every day. By keeping my goal simple and achievable, I find it easier to hit it and in turn that helps me keep my momentum going. I'll switch it up with swimming and cycling, too, but essentially I am doing something I enjoy, with people I want to be with. So, if you love Thai kickboxing, then knock yourself out (or your opponent!). You're more likely to stick with it because you're having fun.

I remember trying yoga with a friend of mine, and it was pretty funny because I am not very bendy-flexy. I enjoyed the company and the laughs (especially when we would fart our way through the class . . .) I didn't care that I stank at it: I was joining in and that was enough.

Mental fitness, such as keeping positive and having a clear mind so I can think quickly, is really important to me. Keeping learning at any age is part of the way I keep my mind active. An active mind is a healthier one, particularly as we age. I find that practising my internal beauty must-haves really helps because I need to feel good about myself and the world, and these things all help with that.

I try to roll with the general punches of life rather than to get too stressed. Being this way keeps me feeling happier about everything. If you feel that life's kicking the crap out of you, maybe you need help with your mental fitness. Don't hesitate to reach out and get that help from either friends or family or even a paid therapist. We've all been there at one time or another. It's the brave and kind thing to do for yourself.

Without a doubt being fit helps with our external and internal beauty. It's a must-do.

habit #5

be
relaxed

When I'm stressed out, that worried frown line between my eyes is really obvious. My face isn't relaxed and neither is my body. I'd bet my blood pressure is up and everything and anybody seems to irritate me. I seriously need to chill out. In fact, I think most of us do!

We all know that being stressed is not good for our internal health: running our bodies constantly on emergency mode can cause headaches, fatigue and affect our mood. What you may not realise is that it also affects your skin, which is your body's largest organ. Stress can contribute to skin issues such as rosacea and eczema, and research suggests it's associated with acne.

We tend to take shorter breaths when stressed and fewer long, leisurely, deep ones. This may lead to increased redness and flushing in our faces, as we are effectively holding our breath. There are also the unconscious body movements we make when stressed, such as frowning, pursing our lips, biting our nails and even sucking on our hair. (I'll never forget a girl I went to school with who constantly sucked on the ends of her hair – not tasty!) Long-term habitual frowning may eventually lead to wrinkles, as the repeated action forms a fine line that can get deeper as we age. I am proof of that as I have a very obvious glabella, or frown line, sitting right smack bang in the middle of my eyebrows. Sometimes, if I'm home alone, I'll put a piece of sticky tape over my frown line to remind me not to – it feels uncomfortable but it's pretty funny.

We need to make the time to relax and be still in the world. Meditation and yoga are excellent starting points. Usually a massage works wonders for me (except for the one that I got in Shanghai, which was a slapping massage – not a relaxing massage, YOW! And I couldn't even tell her to stop because of the language barrier . . . OMG, so painful). Maybe a long bath, a sleep-in or a lie in the hammock will help you. Simple stuff. Stuff that makes you feel good.

My favourite remedy when I'm feeling stressed is getting outside and going for a walk. It calms me down every time. The effects of prolonged stress include depression, anxiety and total burnout, and some of my friends have even experienced quite severe hair loss as a result. So not only are you stressed out, but now you're losing your hair, your skin is probably looking dull as you're not sleeping well . . . aaaaahh! It's a vicious cycle.

Think about what you enjoy and make the time for yourself. It's not being indulgent; it's looking after your health.

habit #6

be nutritious

'let food be thy medicine and medicine be thy food.'
– hippocrates

There was a time when I did not make myself a priority. I was diagnosed as morbidly obese and I had a fatty liver and hypertension. I was a medical disaster and I had a big fat problem: my weight. After a few too many health scares from my doctor, I decided to do something about it. I wrote about this journey in my first book, *The Little Book of Big Weightloss*. Without a doubt, the journey from unhealthy me to curvy-but-definitely-slimmer-and-way-healthier me has made me feel far more beautiful, inside and out. The knock-on effect on my skin has been extraordinary, too. You don't need to have a weight issue to be unhealthy. There are many other ways to compromise your health. Smoking, excessive drinking and party drugs will all contribute towards ageing yourself more quickly than you need to. Of course, we all socialise and occasionally have a few drinks and that's fine. As long as you're not throwing back a bottle of wine every night and your recycling doesn't consist mostly of empty vodka bottles, then all good. We've gotta live, right!

It's about moderation and being healthy most of the time, not all of the time – so of course, at birthdays and holiday times I will relax my rules. But in essence, I do feel so much better living this way and one of the most common comments that I have received time and again is not only on the weight loss, but also on the fact that my skin is glowing and I look like I have turned the clock back fifteen years. Woohoo!

nutritionally, the major things that i do to feel and look great are:

- **Eat whole foods** – these are foods that don't need a label, like vegetables, fruit, fish, etc.
- **Consume very little sugar**
- **Avoid sweet fizzy drinks**
- **Limit the amount of red meat I eat to once a week and eat small amounts of lean protein like fish and chicken**
- **Eat a mostly vegetable-based diet with lots of leafy greens**
- **Eat far fewer processed foods including takeaways**
- **Eat the whole fruit rather than juicing it, for added fibre**
- **Eat far fewer processed carbs like pasta and white bread**
- **Eat good fats like salmon, sardines, avocado and nuts**
- **Drink green tea over any other tea**
- **Stay away from 'diet foods' and read all my food labels**
- **Choose wholegrain bread rather than the processed white kind**
- **Take apple cider vinegar for good gut health**
- **Stop eating at 7 p.m. and don't eat till 10 a.m. – i am fasting overnight in order to give my body a well-needed break so it has time to repair itself**

habit #7

look after your gut

There is mounting evidence that many of our ailments and health problems may be at least partly related to the gut – autoimmune conditions, diabetes, heart conditions and obesity are all on the table for discussion. After all, the gut is home to around 70 per cent of our immune system and is where we absorb many of our nutrients, so if we're not feeding it healthy fuel then it's harder for us to keep running at peak fitness.

Modern science has provided cures for many diseases that we suffer from, but an unfortunate side effect of this success is that we may be compromising our gut health when we take some of those miraculous medicines. They can have a dramatic effect on our gut, obliterating healthy bacteria as well as the problematic bacteria. Many of us have taken antibiotics at one time or another and experienced digestive issues as a consequence. It's not fun.

Some of the common signs that the gut may be out of whack include bloating, diarrhoea, constipation and an irritable bowel, and researchers are also investigating whether some skin problems go hand in hand with poor gut health. The good news is that we can do a lot to

trust your gut, it's smarter than you think.

improve the clarity of our skin through maintaining a healthy diet.

There is emerging evidence that what is in our best interests in our gut is diverse microbes. Think of your gut like a cottage garden: it needs a little bit of everything in order to have good bacteria flourishing. As for health in general, humans benefit from a diverse diet high in fibre-rich whole foods – think fresh fruit and vegetables rather than processed foods, and of course cut back on sugars, alcohol and junk food.

Prebiotic foods like garlic, onion, apples, bananas, oats and cacao may be of particular benefit for optimal health. Fermented foods which are *probiotics* like sauerkraut, kimchi, pickles and yoghurt could also help promote diverse gut flora. Prebiotics (non-digestible fibre) provide the 'fuel' for probiotics (live bacteria) to get to work. I also take one tablespoon of apple cider vinegar diluted in water when I remember. Truly I can't remember the last time I had to take pills – I guess that means my gut is good! I achieve that through varied healthy eating and the occasional probiotic supplement, though if you're having persistent issues with your gut I'd recommend going to see your doctor.

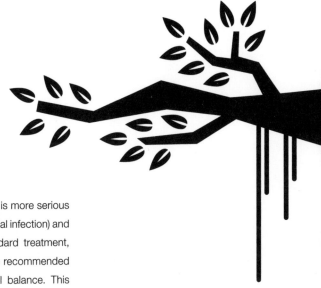

If the trouble with your gut is more serious (such as a recurrent bacterial infection) and is not responsive to standard treatment, a faecal transplant may be recommended to help replenish bacterial balance. This is when the strained and tested poo from someone else's healthy gut gets transplanted into your gastrointestinal tract by means of an enema or massive syringe – they are also experimenting with taking it orally in capsule form, or via a feeding tube. Pretty extreme. Pass me the yoghurt . . .

it's not about the $$$, it's about what works for you.

that's why you need the knowledge about what to buy and how to apply these products. i haven't included specific brands here because at the end of the day, many of the expensive brands manufacture in the same factories as the cheaper brands – so it's the same product, just packaged differently. i know: shock-horror!

if you know what to look for, you can choose your own level of expense. realistically, i can make you look just as good with bargain products as i can with the most expensive lotions and potions. it truly comes down to knowledge, so that's exactly what i'm giving you here.

this little section is going to empower you to make smart, beautiful choices for yourself.

outer beauty
the knowledge you need

your face structure

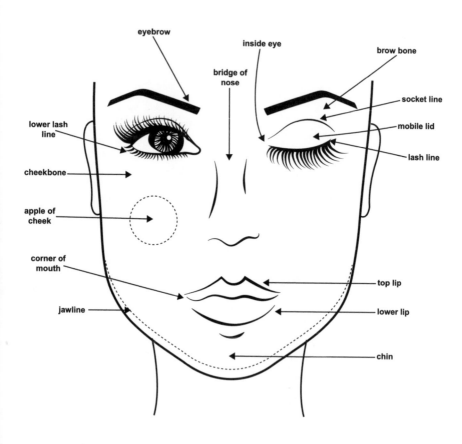

- eyebrow
- inside eye
- brow bone
- bridge of nose
- socket line
- mobile lid
- lower lash line
- lash line
- cheekbone
- apple of cheek
- corner of mouth
- top lip
- jawline
- lower lip
- chin

moisturiser

there are a million different moisturisers on the market with a million different promises to them, and the bottom line is: they mostly do exactly the same thing.

 **what is it?**

A moisturiser's job is to trap water in between the layer it forms and the skin. This is called hydration and it's done with occlusive agents, which help prevent the release of water. Moisturiser also smooths out rough skin with emollients and attracts some moisture (H_2O) with humectants. So basically, a moisturiser supplies a bit of water within its ingredients and then locks that water into your skin with a waxy seal. The most effective waxy seal is petroleum jelly, followed by lanolin, mineral oils and then silicones.

Moisturising will help with dry skin, as it can lock in moisture temporarily. It has nothing to do with the oiliness of your skin, as this is mostly determined by the sebaceous glands that sit just under the skin layer, with oils being secreted through your pores. Like many of the characteristics of your skin, oiliness is hereditary. Oil does keep skin moist and smooth, which helps with wrinkles, but more importantly try to keep hydrated by drinking water.

Some moisturisers claim to increase the collagen in the skin, but collagen molecules are too large to penetrate our skin, so this is a false claim. You might be surprised to learn that a moisturiser will only last about two hours on your skin – at best. This means you'll need to reapply six or so times during the day if you want to keep properly moisturised.

It's nearly impossible to tell the difference between moisturisers because there is a lack of reputable clinical and efficacy testing – plus the claims by cosmetic companies are so numerous.

Honestly, if there was a magic product that cured wrinkles and was anti-ageing, we would all know about it!

At the end of the day you're mostly paying for hype and packaging. When I spoke to cosmetic chemists about this, they told me that the packaging often costs more than the ingredients contained in the bottle – an average bottle of moisturiser costs about $1 to prepare. They all stressed that price is absolutely not an indication of an effective moisturiser, and that a simple ingredient list is often the best. Your sunscreen will usually do the same moisturising job as a dedicated facial moisturiser, especially if it's a sunscreen for the face.

⊕ how to

There are many different ways to moisturise, the most traditional one being with a lotion or cream. Sunscreens often contain moisturising properties, so occasionally on the weekend I will only use a sunscreen. I moisturise twice a day: once in the morning with a tinted moisturiser to even out my skin tone and to provide sunscreen, then once before bed when I apply a facial oil. I use both all over my face and neck, and all the way down to my upper chest area.

 smart choice

Many moisturisers contain vitamins but usually the quantity found in a moisturiser is not enough to make a difference, plus many vitamins become inactive with light and exposure to oxygen. Some vitamins that have been demonstrated to have potent antioxidant and anti-inflammatory properties are vitamins E (alpha-tocopherol), C (L-ascorbic acid), A (retinol) and B3 (niacinamide). I think the most effective of these is B3 (niacinamide), which has been shown to improve skin elasticity and the appearance of wrinkles and yellowing. If buying E or C, try to buy them as a mix as there's evidence to suggest they're more effective when combined than individually.

 pro tip

Use a vitamin E capsule as a face mask: prick the capsule, gently rub the liquid all over your face and leave to absorb. I do this once a week.

facial oils

i only buy 100 per cent organic oil.

❓ what is it?

Oils are good for all types of skin, from oily to dry – it might seem counterintuitive but it's true. They contain varying amounts of omega-3, omega-6 and omega-9, plus a range of vitamins. Broadly speaking, oils higher in omega-9 are good for people with dry skin, while oils higher in omega-6 are good for people with oilier skin and work well as cleansing oils. Those rich in omega-3 are said to be good for skin repair.

oil cleansers

There are many oil cleansers on the market and what I love about cleansing with an oil is that my skin doesn't feel as dry or tight afterwards as when I have used an alcohol- or astringent-based cleanser. Don't use micellar water for cleansing – time and again, cosmetic chemists tell me that it is basically watered down body wash and will strip your face of all oils, which is not a good thing even if you have oily skin.

argan oil

best for dry skin

avocado oil

good for dry skin and one of the highest in omega-9

brazil nut oil

great for dry, ageing skin and high in omega-3 and -9

chia seed oil

very high in omega-3 so good for repair, soothing and protection against ageing

coconut oil

good for medium to dry skin

cranberry seed oil

a well-balanced oil with omega-3, -6 and -9, making it perfect for medium skin

emu oil

good for medium–dry skin as it's high in omega-9

grapeseed oil

good for oily skin and when used as a cleanser

hazelnut oil

very high in omega-9, good for dry skin

hemp oil

high in omega-6, making it good for oily, sensitive skin

macadamia nut oil

best for dry skin as it's high in omega-9

marula oil

one of the highest in omega-9 so good for dry skin

pumpkin seed oil

good for oily skin and an excellent cleanser

red raspberry seed oil

high in omega-6 and -3 with a touch of omega-9, and has a natural SPF

rosehip oil

my go-to oil, it's high in omega-6 and -3 and good for combination skin

safflower oil

very high in omega-6, good for cleansing

homemade oil cleanser

Three parts pumpkin seed oil to one part rosehip oil (or just use straight hemp oil). Either estimate the proportion in the palm of your hand just before use or, if you like, mix a larger amount and get a dedicated bottle to keep it in.

⊕ how to

I use facial oil as a night-time 'moisturiser', applying it all over my face and neck and massaging well into any particularly wrinkly and dry areas. I really like doing this as I wake up the next morning feeling very hydrated, and I particularly like that I am not putting chemicals on my skin as I only buy 100 per cent natural oils. They also last longer than the typical two hours of protection provided by a moisturiser. You can try out the different oil mixes that are available to find your favourite, or if you want to save yourself the dollars you can easily mix your own.

method:

1. Take a clean face cloth, soak it in warm water and place over your face for about ten seconds.
2. Massage cleansing oil into your face and then remove with warm face cloth.
3. Rinse face cloth and repeat as needed.
4. Finish by soaking face cloth in cool water and wiping it across your face to close your pores.

 smart choice

Try rosehip oil, hemp oil or argan oil as a good starting point, as these are all cosmetic oils. Some omega oils can be taken orally and will help your skin, including fish oil. Just don't drink the cosmetic oils – you will need to buy food grade for that! See your pharmacist for the correct omega supplement for you.

pro tip

Oils can also be used for great results on hair – I like an even mix of coconut oil and castor oil. Use sparingly and only from the ears down so you don't end up with an oily scalp. It's a good way to smooth out flyaways and gives a shine to the hair. After applying my facial oil at night, I run the excess oil on my hands through the ends of my hair to give them a quick moisture boost.

foundation

❷ what is it?

Foundation is a tinted cosmetic that is spread across the face to even out skin tone, add or decrease shine and luminosity, and sometimes protect skin from the sun. (It is not designed to correct dark circles or other flaws, which is what concealer is for – for more on concealer, see page 98.) Foundations mostly contain water, oil, silicone and talc and come in various levels of coverage.

tinted moisturiser/BB cream/ CC cream

These are the lightest and generally the most luminous foundations, and are incredibly popular. BB stands for 'Beauty Balm' or 'Blemish Balm' – depending on which country you're in – while CC stands for 'Colour Correcting'. They are essentially all very similar products, they're just marketed to sound different. They almost always have an SPF of at least 15 and are available in a smaller range of colours than a liquid foundation. I use a tinted moisturiser as my daily foundation as it is simple to use, provides a very nice glow to my skin and I like the fact that it has a built-in SPF. It's also very kind to wrinkles. Apply with your fingers; you can also use one of these under your liquid foundation.

light/sheer liquid foundation

These are available in oil-free, matt, luminous and various other confusing labels such as long-lasting and age-defying. The bottom line with a liquid foundation is that you need an SPF in it because most of the damage caused to your skin is by the sun. The next choice is how shiny you want to be – or not. If you have oily skin, I would recommend a more matt foundation and for dry skin a luminous foundation is best. These are the most popular foundations for the general public to use as they are easy to apply and come in a great range of colours. Apply with your fingers or an acrylic foundation brush.

cream/full coverage foundation

These are the heaviest forms of foundation and are the waxiest in feel. They usually come in a stick or cream and cover up the skin to a large degree. Translucency – how much you see the skin through the foundation – is reduced greatly. Cream and full coverage foundations can sit in wrinkles, which is not great if you are older, whereas on a younger face they may make the skin look more 'flawless'. Apply them with a sponge or acrylic foundation brush, though fingers are fine too.

mineral/brush-on foundation

Mineral makeup is essentially ground-up minerals like talc, iron oxides and zinc oxides. Generally considered good for oily skin, this type of foundation comes in powder form to be brushed on with a large, soft powder brush. Coverage is about the same as a light foundation. Those who are fans of mineral foundation tend to prefer it for its dryness.

The main difference from liquid foundation is that mineral foundation generally doesn't contain waxes or oils and is usually fragrance-free – you are essentially brushing onto your face what is in foundation but without the binders and oils or waxes, so it's just dryer.

⊕ how to

When purchasing a foundation, keep these factors in mind:

SPF buy one with a minimum of SPF 15 for sun protection

coverage how opaque the product is (see above)

effect is it luminous, matt or somewhere in between (satin)?

colour get one that correctly matches your skin

choosing the right colour

Usually, foundation colours are divided up into cool and warm tones. This means that some foundations are pinker and some are more yellow. It is notoriously hard to choose the correct colour for yourself when you are standing in an artificially illuminated makeup store – it's just impossible to see colours correctly in there.

This is the reason you need to put your sample foundation near your jawline – in fact, put as much on your face as you are able to. Then walk outside into the fresh air and take a look in a hand-held mirror. Give it about five minutes to see if the colour changes, sometimes it does. It should be extremely close to your skin colour and practically disappear. If you can see a line or mark then it is the wrong colour. Go back and try again.

Many cosmetic houses offer free samples so you can take home different colours to try. Do it. Don't impulse buy a foundation. Unless you love a pretty bottle or a designer name, price is not an indication of a good foundation. While I don't hesitate to pay a bit more for one I like, I just don't pay that money with the mistaken conviction that it is better because it is expensive – get it?

✔ smart choice

There is a foundation that I keep in my kit that is light and quite matt in effect. I found out from someone within the manufacturing cosmetics company that it is also rebranded and sold under a much cheaper label – exactly the same, except for the packaging. And that is the story with much of makeup: identical products in different bottles. Keep that in mind when shopping. Price is not a guarantee of a good product; you're looking for one that suits you.

I'd go for a tinted moisturiser for day wear and a liquid foundation for when you want a little more coverage. You could even mix them to get a coverage that's in between. Our skin changes colour from winter to summer, which is why I always own two foundations: one matches the lightest colour I'll be in winter and the other matches the darkest I'll be in summer. During the year, I mix the foundations in different amounts to create a new in-between colour.

By the way, the term 'hypoallergenic' means whatever the cosmetic company wants it to mean. It doesn't mean it's better for sensitive skin. And something marketed as good for 'mature skin' is not better because maturity is not a skin type.

don't be sucked in by the advertising!

 pro tips

To make your foundation look more even, blend it past your jawline and down your neck, and even onto your chest area.

When you want a lighter look, try buffing your foundation with a soft powder brush to remove excess foundation.

To get added glow, mix your foundation with a dab of shimmer cream.

correctors and concealers

❓ what are they?

These are some of the most important products you can buy – they are essential for creating a flawless look. Things like red skin, dark circles, skin spots and pigmentation marks all get corrected with these amazing little products. I've even covered tattoos with concealer! It is an absolute must-have product.

Concealers can come in palettes, wheels, single and double pots, pens, pencils, tubes and sticks. They are essentially a foundation with more clay in them. They can be mixed in with highlighters and primers or used straight. A concealer is made more for targeting a specific blemish or flaw, whereas a corrector is a less strong overall fixer. So I may conceal my dark under-eye shadows with a concealer and I will correct my red skin with a correcting primer.

correctors

Primers can be used as a base for correcting or brightening overall skin colour because some primers have a hint of correcting colour in them – a green, pink or purple tint. This enables them to counteract the 'flaw' in your skin and make the overall colour more consistent. So, if your complexion is more yellow and you want your skin to appear brighter, a pinkish or lavender tint to your primer is a good thing. With skin that is too ruddy or red, a primer with a green tint to it will act as a veil to the redness. This kind of primer generally goes on first before foundation (but after moisturiser). See page 145 for more on primers.

corrector/highlighting pens

These are incredibly popular, usually in a push-button form – the brush tends to be acrylic and the liquid oozes to the centre when a button on the bottom of the pen is pushed. They come in many colours and are basically a light concealer with a bit of highlight mixed in. They can be pricey and vary in effectiveness. Test them on your skin when purchasing – you may find you want a slightly orangey or pink one to touch up your dark circles. They cover less than straight concealer, but the same colour principles apply.

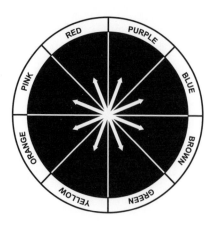

⊕ how to

I find it handy to think of my makeup like a paint palette, and the colour of the concealer is important. Concealers are generally a thicker or more opaque cream that goes directly onto the flaw, and the colour of the concealer on the colour wheel needs to be directly opposite the colour of the flaw to conceal it successfully – that's how they work. Most concealers you see have a touch of the correcting colour within them – they are not solidly this colour.

for red marks use a greenish concealer

for purple or bluish bruising use a yellow concealer

for bluish brown circles (e.g. around the eyes) use an orangey pink concealer

for brown marks use a pinkish orange concealer

for yellow marks use a purple or mauve-tinted concealer

Once you've selected the right colour concealer, apply it on top of your foundation to correct the 'flaw'.

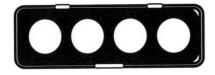

✓ smart choice

 pro tips

I find it useful to have a concealer wheel or palette as I am usually correcting more than one colour flaw on a face so this gives me multiple options. I like a dense cream consistency as I can control how thickly I put it on with a small brush. Then, to blend it, I almost always use my fingers as they are warm and help work it into the skin – it's almost like a little tapping motion on my face, just blending the edges rather than smearing it around. While concealers would be my preference over correcting pens, a correcting pen is handy to keep in your bag for touch-ups.

Lighten up the shadows at either end of your mouth where your mouth either tilts up or down using a slightly lighter shade than your skin tone – it will make you appear 'happier'!

Correcting pens can be a breeding ground of bacteria, so wash them weekly in detergent and dry them without the cap on.

highlighters and shimmer powders

❷ what are they?

Highlighters and shimmer powders 'highlight' an area by drawing the eye to that area of the face. They are effectively foundation formula with different tints or colours in them and added mica – an ingredient that makes them reflect the light. Like foundation, they come in either a liquid, stick or powdered form. The powdered form of highlighter is also called a shimmer powder and comes as pressed or loose powder to be applied with a brush. (Pressed powders are easier to use and less messy – loose powders can get everywhere if you're not careful!)

liquid and stick highlighters

Highlighters are used on top of or mixed into a foundation to add glamour, shine and a light sparkle to makeup – so they're especially nice to wear at night. When used correctly, they make the face look really fresh and healthy, and they can also help with adding dimension to a flat face (see more on this in Contouring, page 106).

The downside to highlighters is that if you have very oily skin they can make you appear sweaty. They're also not your friend if you have overly wrinkled or damaged skin as they can emphasise fine lines and acne scarring. For this reason, they tend to work better on younger skin (under thirty-

five years) with fewer wrinkles. Basically, the better your skin is the stronger you can go with a highlighter.

All three types of highlighter come in various tones: pale pink or peachy, silvery or white, and shades of gold, bronze or copper. See next page for tips on colour selection.

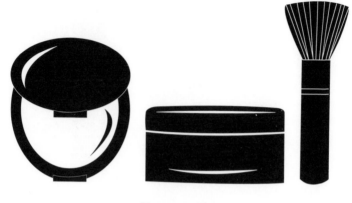

shimmer powders

⊕ how to

Choose the colour of your highlighter based on your skin tone – the correct choice will 'lift' the skin, making it appear more luminous. Pale skin usually looks better with a pink or silvery highlighter whereas medium beige or yellow-toned skin looks good with a pinky, peachy or light gold highlighter. Darker skin looks amazing with a warm highlighter such as a gold, bronze or copper colour.

The liquid and stick forms can be applied with your finger or directly drawn onto your face and blended. Liquid highlighter can also be mixed with your own foundation to obtain a very glowy look all over the face. Be careful of doing this if it is hot or you are having photography done, though, as you could look extremely sweaty! Start off with a ratio of 80 per cent foundation to 20 per cent highlighter and mix well on the back of your hand before applying. The stronger the highlighter, the less you need.

Alternatively, use a highlighter on specific areas. To highlight cheekbones (the most common use), apply it on the highest part of your cheekbone and blend out. Start

highlighter application areas

A stick highlighter is very user-friendly and travels well in your makeup bag, plus it can be used on both younger and older skin. If you have very oily skin, use a pressed shimmer powder instead.

🐰 pro tips

Mix a little highlighter with a crème blush (see page 112) and apply on the apple of the cheek – it makes you look amazingly fresh and healthy.

Dab a tiny dot of highlighter onto the inner corner of your eye to make you appear fresher and more 'awake', and put it on the high point of your brow bone under the eyebrow to emphasise your eyes.

off with just a little and add – it's the best way to avoid mistakes. Sometimes I add a highlight down the centre of my nose to create a straighter-looking nose (avoid this if you don't want to draw attention to your nose). You can also highlight your cupid's bow in a V shape to draw attention to your mouth. The shoulders, collarbones and the top round of your breasts are all areas that look good highlighted, too. Loose powders are good if you are highlighting shoulders and body parts and want a lot of powder on your brush – apply with a medium or large powder brush.

contouring

❓ what is it?

Contouring is the strategic practice of light and shade: using shading to draw back certain areas of the face and highlighting to bring out or bring forward other areas. It can dramatically change the structural appearance of your face and enhance your best features when done well.

CONTOUR PALETTE

Contouring is hugely popular because it's so flattering, and it can be really effective if you know how – but it can also be tragic if you don't. It's actually as old as time – the theatre has been using contouring for decades, and I've been contouring on models for years – but fashion has just made it really big recently so that more people are doing it themselves.

Contour powders and contour creams usually come in a palette form as you need multiple and contrasting colours to create the sculptured and shaped look. A palette usually contains one darker or shading powder, one highlighting powder and a blush. Powders are possibly an easier way to start as they give softer definition – and the key to successful contouring is to keep it looking subtle and natural. Powders are usually a slightly greyer shade than a bronzer, but only slightly. A highlighting colour can be anything from gold to peach to white.

After you have put on your foundation, take two brushes, angled in shape, one slightly larger than the other. The larger brush is for the contour (shadow) and the smaller is for the highlighter. Don't use the same brush to do both as you will end up with a dirty mess! Start off with a little bit of contour on your big brush – you can always add more but it's harder to remove excess. Brush it onto the areas on your face as shown in the pictures on the next page – follow the grey shading guidelines on the face shape that corresponds closest to your own as these are where shadow would most naturally fall on your face. When you're done, pick up your clean smaller brush, dip it in your highlighting colour and apply in the white areas shown in the pictures overleaf – remembering that less is more.

When you've finished highlighting, blend the two areas together with a third soft, large brush. Voilà: contoured perfection!

square face

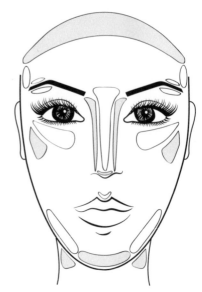

long face

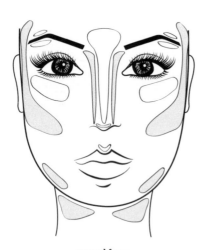

round face

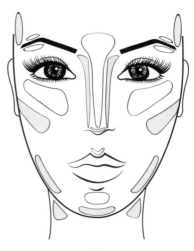

oval face

triangle face

contouring the nose

✔ smart choice

To pick your colours, look for a contour cream or powder that is a couple of shades darker than your actual skin and a highlighting colour that's a shade lighter than your skin. I find that this ratio of two shades darker, one shade lighter works well as it creates enough of a contrast for the contouring to be effective without getting too far away from your natural skin tone and looking like dirty marks on your skin.

🎩 pro tip

Contour your breast area by creating a large M-shaped shadow and then highlighting on the peak of your breasts. This trick makes them appear rounder and is used on many a TV and movie set!

blush

❓ what is it?

Blush is used to contour and add colour to
your face, and is primarily applied on the
cheek area to give a natural healthy glow.

powder blush

These pressed powders come in a variety of sizes and a million colours, as well as either matt or illuminating (sparkly). The pigment or strength of the colour can vary greatly – a blush that has less pigment can be easier to use as you'll make fewer mistakes but you may end up a bit powdery, so choose one with a decent amount of colour that you feel you can move. Make sure you try before you buy – as a general rule, a fair complexion looks great with a pink-toned blush and a warmer skin tone looks fantastic with a bronze or peach-toned blush. When selecting your colour, try it on the back of your hand – or even better, your face, because that's ultimately where it is going to go.

It's important that the blush can spread easily on the face as you don't want to end up with spots of blush that have grabbed onto your cheeks – you may end up with spots of colour rather than a soft look! To prevent that happening, powder lightly with a translucent powder first. When applying powdered blush, use an angled powder brush and be careful if you are putting it on top of a moisturiser as it will tend to 'grab.' A crème blush will not grab and if you have a particularly dewy foundation this could be the better choice for you.

Bronzers are part of this group as they are really just a brown blush. You can use bronzer as a contour powder, a blush and even an eyeshadow – it's a versatile product with many applications. Try brushing bronzer underneath your jawline, working from ear to ear, as this will sharpen your jawline. I'd recommend only doing this when you know you're going to be in soft light, such as at night.

crème blush

These usually come in pots with lids or occasionally in a tube or a stick. They are very user-friendly and very easily create a fresh look. They tend not to be loaded with pigment so they slide on well and can be moved around the face easily. You can also use them to double up as a lip cream.

gel blush

Gel blush feels a bit waterier than a crème blush and usually comes in a tube or pot. It is mostly fairly subtle in tone and sometimes requires layers of application to achieve the effect. Because of their fairly sheer look, gel blushes are good if you want a light, fresh feel and don't like a cream.

⊕ how to

Smile in the mirror and notice the 'apples' of your cheeks – these are the parts that are pushed forward and round when you smile. Apply a touch of your chosen blush there for a fresh and natural look.

✔ smart choice

A crème blush is very flattering to nearly every skin type plus it looks fresh, is super easy to use and can be carried in your bag without the worry of breakage. I usually always have a bronzer, a favourite apricot blush and a rosy pink blush handy – they're essential for looking fresh and healthy.

pro tips

Use your bronzer to contour your face (see page 107), then place a small amount of a pink or apricot blush on the apple of your cheek to create a sculpted yet natural look.

You can also mix two different blushes together to create a new and different shade.

eyeshadow

❓ what is it?

I love eyeshadow; it is truly transformative. A great eyeshadow can really make your eyes 'pop' by making them look larger and sexier and enhancing the colour of your iris. One thing I try to keep in mind with makeup is to experiment and try new looks, and eyeshadow is an easy and low-risk way to mix things up. If you have brown eyes, give an orangey copper shadow a go. Try a silver, brown or grey on blue eyes; and green eyes look amazing with purple or bronze shadows. Don't be shy to try, you can always wipe it off!

Eyeshadows can come as pressed powder, loose powder, pots, tubes or crayons.

It's all about pigment with eyeshadow, which is the amount of colour within the eyeshadow. When looking for a good eyeshadow, test it on the back of your hand – if the colour comes up similar to how it looks in the palette, then it has enough pigment in it. Price is not always an indication of how much pigment a shadow has – there are some awesome cheaper brands that contain heaps of pigment. A matt shadow looks good on everyone, a lightly sparkly shadow works on anyone when used sparingly and metallic shadows should be used with care on anyone over the age of forty as the way they catch the light can emphasise wrinkles.

powder

Powder shadows usually come in a palette or compact for application with a small foam brush that is often pretty useless – so do yourself a favour and buy a small domed bristle-head eyeshadow brush to use. Shadows are available in matt, sparkly or various degrees of metallic. There are loose powders, too, which can be a bit tricky to use because they're harder to control but have a nice finish because the pigment concentration is strong.

crème

Crème eyeshadows come in pots, tubes and crayons. They're a waxier form of eyeshadow and can look fantastic as the colour is usually fairly intense. They tend to be shinier than powder shadows and can be quite metallic. They can be applied either with an acrylic brush or with your finger. You can even put a powder eyeshadow on top of a crème for a more intense look – plus it will increase the longevity of your eyeshadow.

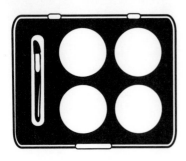

⊕ how to

Before applying eyeshadow, put a small amount of concealer or foundation on the eyelid and smooth it across to get rid of any wrinkles in the skin. If your skin tends to be particularly oily then dust with a powder before applying. Prepping the surface will also help your chosen shadow to stay put. Now you're ready to apply.

The most important thing to remember with eyeshadow is to blend, blend and then blend again. Generally, I find it easiest to start with the lightest colour eyeshadow I'm using first, then add the next darkest shade and then finally the darkest shade. I then go back to the light eyeshadow and blend the edges. It's all about layering – like painting, layering colours will make for a more vibrant look. It will also last longer on your eyes.

here are three basic looks – easy as 1, 2, 3!

1. a wash

Pick just one eyeshadow colour and use it as a 'wash' – in other words, colour the entire mobile lid, starting from close to the lash bed, fading the colour right up to the brow bone, where it will disappear into nothingness. This is a fresh, simple look that's easy to get right, particularly with a lighter eyeshadow – a pale gold is great on many eye colours and skin tones. Follow with mascara (see page 122) to open up your eye.

2. a natural winged eye

Pick two eyeshadows that are complementary, one light and one medium-toned – so maybe soft pink and medium purple, or pale gold and taupe. Place the light shadow all over the eye like a wash, fading up to the eyebrow. Take the medium shadow and brush it along the crease of your eye socket, blending it into the light shadow. Then apply the medium colour with a fine brush along the lash line both above and below the eye, starting about three-quarters of the way along towards the outer corner of the eye and extending it past the corner of the eye into a 'wing'. Finish off with a winged eyeliner (see page 119) and heaps of mascara (see page 122).

3. a sexy smoky eye

Pick three eyeshadows all within the same colour family such as cream, light brown and dark brown. Start with your darkest eyeshadow and apply it along the upper lash line very close to the lash bed, working slowly up and out. If you have close-set eyes, start the dark colour a little further away from the inner corner of the eye. Blend the colour upwards so that it's strongest at your lash line and covers your entire mobile lid, gently fading from dark to light.

Next, take your lightest eyeshadow and sweep it onto your brow bone area, starting to blend it down into the darker eyeshadow. Then dip your brush into the medium colour and place it on the area in your socket line where the other two colours meet. Blend so that your eye makeup goes from dark at your lower lash line to non-existent or very light at your eyebrow. Use a small amount of the darkest eyeshadow dabbed carefully underneath your eye along the lash line to finish off. Complete with a smudged pencil liner (see page 119) and mascara (see page 122).

✅ smart choice

A good 'naturals' palette with at least four neutral tones is a must-have because everyone can use it. Carry a pencil eyeshadow with you in your handbag as it is less likely to break than a powder and doesn't require a brush.

🐰 pro tips

Wet down your brush and then dip it into your eyeshadow – it will become like a paint and will go on more intensely. Wait until it's dried then apply other dry eyeshadows on top of it.

To open up the eye and make you appear fresher, place a touch of white or very light eyeshadow on the inside edge of your eye near your nose, top and bottom.

Do not put your concealer or foundation under your eye area until you have done your eye makeup – this makes it easy to clean up any smudges or dropped shadow without removing the makeup you've just carefully applied! Then finish applying your concealer and foundation for a super clean effect.

eyeliner

❓ what is it?

Eyeliner is used to line the eyes, usually the top lid, to create definition. It can be used as a base for eyeshadow and is sometimes applied to the lower lash line and occasionally inside the inner eye line.

⊕ how to

pencils and roll-up pencils

Generally the softest and most user-friendly way to wear eyeliner. They're the easiest to smudge after putting on and are good for providing a base to eye makeup, plus roll-up pencils have the advantage of not needing to be sharpened all the time. When doing a smoky eye, use a pencil that's darker than your eyeshadow to colour and smudge, then place the eyeshadow on top – it will increase the depth and longevity of your makeup. Pencils can also be used on the inside line (the 'waterline') of the eye (see my Pro Tip on page 121).

felt-tip liners

Fairly unforgiving if you make a mistake, so you need to have a steady hand. Usually they come in limited colours like black and brown and they should last all day, although many are waterproof too – a good choice if your eye makeup is usually prone to smudging. Pick one with a finer point as that will make application easier. I like them for creating a sharp cat's eye look.

To do this, carefully draw an even line three-quarters of the way across your eyelid along the lash line, working from the inside to outside edge, and then stop. From three-quarters of the way across, start angling the line up following the angle of your lower lash line until you have reached a point just past the outside corner of your eye (about 3–5 mm depending how dramatic you'd like the flick). Join up the lines cleanly and go over the whole line if needed to neaten it up, then take a little peek in the mirror. Voilà! A perfect cat's eye.

liquid eyeliner tubes

Little pots of colour that come with a fine-haired brush that dips into the pot; they may look a bit like a mascara in shape. They come in many fun colours, including glittery or metallic, and are a great way to use eyeliner as long as your application skills are good – ideally you need to get it right first go, as mistakes can be hard to correct. Liquid eyeliner can be used underneath eyeshadow – allow time to dry – as well as on top. It's important to buy one with a good brush so try the tester on the back of your hand to see if you like the way the brush works, as some are easier to manipulate than others. In general, you can be bold and go for a sweeping line that travels from the inside of your eye to just past the outside corner of your eye, working upwards as you get closer to the outside edge.

gel eyeliner

Small pots of colour that are best used with a small angled brush. You can build up the colour by going over the line multiple times. They can be used under a smoky eye very easily and can be blended if you're quick. I usually draw the line lightly on the eye first, fix up any mistakes with a cotton bud and then when I'm happy with the shape I go over it again to darken it off.

✔ smart choice

I always have several pencils in various colours plus a felt-tip liner or a really sharp liquid liner because I find I need them both for different looks. I always test the pencils for hardness on the back of my hand before purchasing as I'm looking for a pencil that glides, not pulls. Felt-tip liners and liquid eyeliner tubes are great for young eyes with no wrinkles, while a pencil or gel eyeliner that can be smudged is kinder to an older eye. Blondes may find they like the softer effect of a dark brown or grey eyeliner whereas brunettes may prefer a darker shade like black.

♞ pro tips

Use a white pencil on the lower waterline of the eye to make the eye look fresh and open.

Line the mobile lid with a gel liner and then use a contrasting eyeshadow on top for a velvety, dramatic look. So for example, if you put a black liner on first then smudge it and apply a green eyeshadow, the green that sits on top of the black will turn into a darker khaki colour. It's like painting – the darker colour underneath adds depth to the top layer. You can do this with a million colour combinations. Some good ones to try are black liner and purple eyeshadow, brown liner and gold eyeshadow, or blue liner and green eyeshadow.

Brush a white eyeshadow onto the mobile lid and then get out your blackest felt liner and do a sharp flicked line just extending out past your eye – this will make the black really pop.

mascara

❓ what is it?

Mascara is used to lengthen and thicken your eyelashes while coating them in colour to frame your eyes. Many of the cosmetic chemists I've spoken to tell me that the formula for mascara hasn't changed in fifty years! Wow. That's probably why they're all banging on about the brush, not the formula . . .

Mascara is available in waterproof and non-waterproof. Most of us buy the non-waterproof because in all honesty, sometimes waterproof mascara can be really difficult to remove. That said, waterproof is handy at weddings, on beach holidays or at times when you think you

may cry (or sweat). Waterproof mascara uses the same technology as waterproof sunscreen.

brush

The first thing I look at when selecting a mascara is the brush (or 'wand'): it is the most important factor in purchasing the correct one. I opt for a tapered or narrow brush that can get into the bed of the lashes. A curved brush can be useful as the curve will push up the lashes as you apply the mascara.

Mascara brushes are usually made of either a form of rubber or bristle. It's personal choice but I tend to favour a bristle brush as I find them less rigid. Usually, the smaller and shorter a person's lashes, the thinner the mascara brush they need.

colour

As a general rule, if you have blonde or red hair you probably want a dark brown mascara, whereas if you are brunette or have black hair then a black mascara will be a better match with your natural lash colour. A softer look – good for daytime – is achieved by using a brownish colour, but if you want your lashes to really stand out then choose black.

⊕ how to

Starting at the bed of the lashes, run the mascara wand up until it has reached the ends of your lashes, wiggling it gently as you go for better coverage. Do this across all top lashes, fanning them out to separate them. Apply another coat to the outside edge of your eyelashes in order to lift the eye. Two coats are usually enough. After applying mascara, use a finger to push the lashes up from underneath – this helps with lifting the lashes while they are drying. When applying mascara to the lower lashes, I always remove the excess to give the lashes a less clumpy look – if you don't want to get your finger dirty, use a mascara comb to do this. Most of the time I use mascara only on the top lashes as this creates a sleepy, sexy eye. Applying it to the bottom lashes can sometimes make the eyes look smaller and it has a tendency to rub off.

Mascara is the cosmetic with the shortest lifespan – around three to five months. This is because of the risk of getting eye infections from the bacteria that can breed in the tube. I throw away my mascara as soon as it starts to smell too chemically – so notice the smell when you first buy it. If it changes, it is time to throw it.

✓ smart choice

A brownish-black mascara with a narrow, slightly curved, medium-sized bristle wand is always a good choice. It is universally popular and the brush allows you to get into the harder-to-reach areas. In my experience, price isn't a big factor when shopping for mascara as some of the best ones are the cheapest.

Occasionally you'll see a mascara that has wands at both ends, one white and one black. The white formula contains filaments: tiny little particles within the mascara, usually made of silk or rayon, that lengthen the eyelash when applied. This is a gimmick because most mascaras already have the filaments included within the formula – they just don't advertise it, or they may say the word 'lengthening' as a clue. It's best for people with contact lenses or sensitive eyes to avoid mascara with filaments in it because they can flake off the lashes and irritate the contacts.

🐰 pro tips

Use coloured mascaras to make your eye colour 'pop' by picking a completely contrasting coloured mascara – for example, using a blue mascara on a golden coloured eye. Coloured mascaras are a fun, easy and cost-effective way to change your look.

A hand-held lash curler may look more like a medieval torture device than an instrument of beauty but can make a big difference and really open up your eyes. Use it before mascara, clamping it onto the lashes as close to the lash bed as possible without catching your eyelid. Hold it in place for about ten seconds and then remove. If I have time I might even gently warm the curler up with the hairdryer quickly before using it so that the curl holds a bit more. You can buy battery-powered curlers but I find they are only about as effective as the traditional ones.

If you want to get a good curl to your lashes, the other alternative is to get them permed. It's a really effective solution, especially if your eyelashes grow straight – it lasts about three weeks or so and is very affordable.

false eyelashes

❷ what are they?

False lashes were incredibly popular in the '60s and are huge again now. The good thing is that the technology for them has improved so much – they are far more user-friendly and comfortable to wear these days, which probably accounts for the surge in popularity. There are three ways to artificially enhance your lash thickness and length: the first two are to wear false lashes – either individual pieces or full strips – and the third is to get semi-permanent lash inserts.

✺ how to

individual lashes

Individual lashes come in single, double or even triple lash pieces, and vary in length and colour: short, medium or long; and brown or black. I use the double short black ones most often, though a triple lash is a quick and easy way to apply individuals so I use these if I'm in a hurry.

Always use tweezers to handle and place individual lashes. To apply, dip the root end of the lash into lash glue and then gently place on the lash bed, starting near your inner eye and working outwards. Increase the length of the individual lash used as you work outwards – for example, apply six double short lashes and then finish off with three double medium at the outer corner – as this will lift the corner of the eye up.

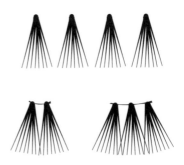

For a feathery, open-eye look, use just single medium lashes and space them a little further apart, using about eight lashes rather than sixteen.

Individual lashes are extremely comfortable to wear – definitely more comfortable than a strip. There are endless ways you can play with them to change the look and shape of your eye, for example:

- **Alternate one short and then one medium lash all along the eye to create a feathery look.**
- **Place medium or long lashes in the middle of the eye (directly above the iris) to create a more rounded eye.**
- **Just add a few longer lashes on the ends of your eye to create a natural kick-up.**

The lashes should simply fall off as you remove your eye makeup but if they don't, you can gently pull them off yourself – it doesn't hurt.

strip lashes

A strip lash is a complete set of lashes all joined together. They come in an enormous range of colours, lengths and thicknesses, from extremely natural to completely crazy, touching-your-eyebrows and glittery. They are great fun. I usually apply with my fingers rather than tweezers. The most important thing to look for is a bendable lash – the fine strip that the lashes are attached to needs to be very flexible as this will allow the lash to follow the curve of your eye and sit comfortably.

on the back of your hand. Bring the lash strip up to your eye while you are looking down – try not to close your eye as you can easily stick your eyelids together! Press the strip as close to the lash bed as possible. I always start in the middle of the eye, then work inwards and do the outside edge last. Full strips can be tricky to get on neatly and the glue takes a couple of minutes to dry but keep trying, as it gets much easier the more you do it. If they're not on properly or look a bit wonky, don't hesitate to rip them off and start again. They are completely reusable, so you can just peel off the glue and retry.

lash glue

The most popular lash glue is latex. It comes in many names and brands, usually with a choice of two colours – clear (which looks white unless dried) or black. I always use clear as it is very forgiving, whereas black can be a little harder to get right. If you're allergic to latex then there are other latex-free glues available.

lash inserts

Lash inserts are semi-permanent individual hairs that are joined onto your own lashes with a glue. Your first appointment can take up to two hours, so be patient! They can be really effective as a 24/7 solution and are

Most strip lashes are long, so before you apply them to the lash bed you'll need to cut them to the right length for your eyes. Pick up the correct lash for the correct eye – they all have a left and right eye – and hold it against your lash bed, noticing where it is too long. Grab some small scissors and cut the excess lash off from the outer end. Note: you do this before placing any glue on the lashes, and only cut the lashes when they are not on your eye as you don't want to go giving your own lashes a trim!

Once your strips are the perfect length, apply a small amount of lash glue along the lash strip and dab any excess glue off great when you're going on holiday but the downside is that they are fairly expensive to have done at $120–250, and the constant costly maintenance needed can set you back around $100 per month. They also have the unfortunate habit of thinning out your own existing lashes.

There are many 'rules' when wearing lash inserts: don't put mascara on them, don't play with them, don't place your face directly into the shower and don't use anything oily near your eyes (including moisturiser). It's also important that you don't sleep with your face in the pillow – so yep, lots of rules!

I think they're a good option if you have something really special happening, like your honeymoon, and you want to look super lashy every hour of the day. They usually last about four to five weeks but by that time you'll have probably lost half of them and need a refill – so another appointment and another two hours. And if you want them taken off properly with remover gel, you will need another appointment. They're pricey little buggers!

 **smart choice**

Use short triple individual lashes in black for a quick and easy-to-apply lash extension.

Avoid magnetic eyelashes – they haven't yet been designed in a way that sits properly on the eye, so I give them a miss.

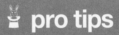 **pro tips**

Colour in the lash bed with eyeliner when wearing false lashes as this makes the join disappear. I always use mascara after I have applied lashes as it helps join up the false and real lashes together for a more natural look.

Use a strip lash as a base and fill in where you want more with individual lashes – so you could try adding medium individuals on top towards the outer edge of your eye to create an almond-shaped eyev. I've also been known to put on two strip lashes, one on top of the other, for an extreme lash look. Finish with an eyeliner.

eyebrows

whether it's a structured brow or a natural bushy brow that you're after, there are a few tools that are handy for the job.

Eyebrow fashions come and go. In the '70s we plucked them into thin lines and by the '80s we were praying they had grown back into the bushy brows that had then become popular. We can shape them to make our eyes look more open or further apart and to generally flatter our facial features. If you have close-set eyes you can clean up between your brows to create the illusion of more space, and the reverse is true too: if your eyes are wide set you may want to keep your eyebrows sitting a bit closer together. If you have large eyes you may find that heavier brows balance them off, whereas if your eyes are smaller you may want to keep them a little lighter on your face.

There aren't really any hard and fast rules; it comes down to how you like your brows to look. But remember they can drastically change your face, so before you get busy plucking grab a white pencil and go over the hairs you think you don't need and stand back and take a look – it will give you a good indication of the final result.

If you find that you have no idea what will be the most flattering shape for your face then go see a professional and get them done properly once. You can maintain the finished brow easily with an angled pair of tweezers, just tidying them up when those little hairs pop through. Weekly is often more than enough to keep them in check.

must-have eyebrow tools

- An angled brush with a wand at the end
- An angled pair of tweezers and a piece of ice (for numbing) for plucking out those pesky short hairs
- A sharp pair of small scissors for trimming the top of your brows if the hairs are long

⊛ how to

eyebrow gel

Eyebrow gels are handy for a fairly natural look. They usually come with a wand like the one you find in a mascara, which you use like a brush to coat the eyebrow hairs so the gel, once dry, holds them in place. The colours range from clear to brown and black: a clear gel can be used on top of an eyebrow pencil to keep brows in place, while the tinted gels will coat the eyebrows with a colour for the day.

eyebrow pencil

Great for natural-looking brows. Keep in mind to use these lightly – don't draw! That's not what they're for. Instead, use the brush at the end to brush your hairs into place while flicking on little fake hairs with the pencil in between brushes. Keep a nice sharp point on your pencil, as it will make for a finer line.

eyebrow powder

Useful for anyone wanting a natural-looking or structured brow. Most eyebrow powder can be used wet or dry; applying it dry gives a softer look. Brush it on with a small angled brush. Many eyebrow powder sets contain more than one colour, which is handy for creating a structured brow as you can use a darker shade to give a sharp outer end to your brow.

eyebrow wax

Eyebrow wax isn't as forgiving to use as powder but it does have more holding power, as the wax sets the brows in place. It comes in a small pot and is used with an angled brush.

eyebrow stain

Handy for anyone with sparse brows who is time-poor as the stain fills in the brows with colour that lasts a few days. Some peel-off stains can be slept in and then removed the next morning. The benefit of these is that it will look from a distance as if your brows are very manicured, but the negative is that up close they can look a bit fake.

 # smart choice

Your best buy is an eyebrow powder palette with at least two different colours that comes with an angled brush because it can be used for both natural-looking and more structured brows. Plus, the darker colour can be used to sharpen ends where the hair naturally fades out, and it can usually be used wet or dry. It's a winner!

pro tips

Sometimes lightening your brow colour can make your eyes really pop. Use an eyebrow gel that's slightly lighter than your natural eyebrow colour to coat all your eyebrow hairs. Fill in with a light powder of a similar colour using an angled brush and voilà: you'll have structured brows that appear softer on your face.

Another quick trick for unruly brows if you don't have a gel handy is to spray some hairspray onto your eyebrow brush and run it through your brows to hold them in place.

lipstick

yes, lipstick's had a long history – and it's not going anywhere. so, pick your favourite because it's here to stay!

❓ what is it?

Lipstick is used to colour and condition your lips. Some of the first 'lipsticks' ever used were simple stains made from fruits such as berries which, if you think back to being a kid, were something we all improvised with at one time or another. Colouring lips with ochre has also been used to symbolise female sexuality and independence for some Indigenous Australians.

Did you know that about 5000 years ago, ancient Sumerian women used to crush gems and wear them on their face and lips? A bit like the glitter that has found its way into many cosmetics today. Cleopatra wore a striking red colour on her lips, which was made by crushing the female cochineal bug. It sounds pretty gross, but cochineal is actually still used today in cosmetics under the names 'Carmine', 'Crimson Lake', and 'Natural Red 4'. Every time Dita Von Teese comes to town, you'll see me pulling out my red lipsticks because I know that they're going to get a workout when I work on her signature-look models!

We like to think we are all unique and lipstick is an extension of that belief. It can be an expression of our emotions: that red lipstick is commonly associated with a sexy and confident woman. We're telling the world who we think we are, without even knowing it.

⊕ how to

lipstick

The most popular makeup item of them all, the classic lipstick is affordable, available in a million colours and very portable in its cute little packaging. Made mostly from waxes and oils with pigment, lipsticks glide on easily and leave behind a brilliant streak of colour. The level of shine ranges from satin to matt.

Matt lipstick is hands down the longest-lasting lipstick around – it's capable of surviving numerous kisses! It comes in either lipstick form or in a tube with sponge applicator, which is commonly known as lip chalk and is without doubt the driest and most matt of the two. The downside is the chalky, dry feeling on your lips and the uneven wear marks – but the plus side of lip chalk is its durability and the density of the colours available. It's usually used without a lip liner and it's fairly easy to go outside your lip line slightly to create a fuller-looking lip.

lip gloss

The shiniest of the lot, lip gloss often comes in a pot or tube and can be applied with your finger or a brush. Apply on top of lipstick for added shine. It is mostly made up of oils and so is hard to keep on your lips for any length of time, but it does make lips look super sexy and can help with keeping your lips moisturised. I find it's good in summer when you want to feel hydrated.

lip stain

Lip stain feels like nothing on your lips but gives them a strong and long-lasting tint that enhances your natural lip colour. Instead of coating your lips, it seeps into your skin – which means it can be drying. Moisturising with a lip balm first can often alleviate the dryness. Especially good for daytime wear, stains come in limited colours and the prettiest ones are often on the spectrum of red, berry and pink. They're commonly packaged as a felt-tip pen or in a small bottle.

lip liner

Usually taking the form of a pencil, this is a denser and waxier form of colour that outlines the shape of your lip and helps lipstick stay in place. It prevents bleeding, increases the longevity of lipstick and can even be worn on its own when the lips are fully coloured in. Choose a colour that is extremely close to your lipstick as this will make for a more seamless effect. Before applying lipstick, use a well-sharpened lip liner to draw around the outline of your lips and then fill them in completely.

✔ smart choice

Carry a matt lipstick in your bag as the colour is vibrant and it's long lasting but it's not as drying as lip chalk. When it comes to lipstick, sometimes the very cheap are good and sometimes the very expensive are good – and sometimes they're the same product, just sold in different packaging by different brands! Personally I love my lipstick to be beautifully packaged so this is where I will tend to splurge, but throughout my career I can say I haven't found price to be a determining factor for durability.

It's handy to own a few natural shades of lip colour, like pinky browns, plus some more statement colours like bright corals, reds and burgundies. Don't worry when your favourite colours get discontinued; it just means you have an opportunity to try something new and with the abundance of colours available it shouldn't be long until you have a new favourite.

 pro tips

Use a slight dab of a lighter lipstick in the middle of your bottom lip and top lip to create the illusion of a fuller set of lips.

After applying lipstick to your lips, dab a finger onto your lips and place the lipstick onto the apple of your cheek: instant colour-coordinated crème blush!

To get that stubborn red lipstick off at night, massage a bit of moisturiser or oil onto your lips and it should start to move.

Place a touch of lip gloss on your eyelids for a super shiny eye.

Mix different lipsticks at will to create instant new colours. If you're not doing this, you're missing out on half of your lipsticks' function! Pick the lipstick that you want mostly to shine through and apply that to your lips first, then grab your second colour and just dab touches of it on top. New colour – yeah! Or try colouring your lips in completely with your lip pencil and then put a contrasting tone on top, being careful to cover the lip pencil totally. You can even mix two colours together on the back of your hand and then apply with a lip brush. Your imagination is really the only constraint you have!

setting sprays and powders

❓ what are they?

Setting sprays and powders encourage your makeup to stay on longer: a spray usually contains a form of silicone, which applies a very thin protective veil to your makeup, while powders contain talc, which matts down your makeup and absorbs the oils from your face.

⊕ how to

setting sprays

These small spray bottles are the new kids on the block and are becoming very popular to keep makeup looking fresh all day. They can either matt you down or give you a luminous look for the day. Many are designed to seal in moisture and some even contain an SPF. They vary greatly in cost but price is not an indicator of effectiveness; just search for one that suits you. Hold your breath and the bottle about 20 cm away from you, then spray lightly over your face.

There are also hydrating sprays on the market, but these usually won't seal in your makeup as they contain more moisturising ingredients like oils. This makes them good to use before applying makeup but not as a makeup setting spray – despite what they may advertise. Don't get confused between the two.

powders

Most powders contain talc, which is a naturally occurring mineral composed of magnesium, silicon, oxygen and hydrogen. Powders will matt down your face and are available in a huge range of styles and colours. Keep powder away from wrinkles as it will only enhance them. Use powders after you have finished doing your makeup. Lightly is best.

If you are fair-skinned, a translucent powder is always a good choice as it has no colour, whereas it can look a bit white on olive or darker skins. If you want a little extra coverage, look for a powder that matches your skin tone. Luckily there are tons of colours to choose from. I choose the finest and softest powder available.

Pressed powder is the classic compact powder that's semi-solid and pressed flat. Pop the compact open and use a brush or puff to apply. Pressed powders are great for travel and on-the-run touch-ups. They make your face look more matt, reduce shine and increase the longevity of your makeup.

Loose powder is pretty much exactly the same thing but only loose, not pressed into a compact, which means it doesn't contain the solidifying ingredients such as silicone and waxes. It does exactly the same job as pressed powder but is messier in your handbag if the lid comes off!

The following four powders can all come in either pressed or loose form.

Setting powder is used to 'set' your makeup in place and reduce shine, and is the most common powder.

Foundation powder is a cross between a setting powder and a foundation, so it has more colour and more coverage than a standard setting powder but is lighter than a liquid foundation. It can be used on its own without a liquid foundation for a light look.

Finishing powder is used after setting powder to 'finish' your makeup. It's designed not to sit in wrinkles and to give a more flawless appearance. Some contain more silicon than a setting powder, which tends to have more talc in it. As finishing powders are white, make sure to blend them well: under powerful camera flashes they can cause the notorious ghostly 'flashback' effect.

High-definition powder is the one to pull out when cameras are around, and a lifesaver for pro makeup artists like me. Mostly translucent in colour, it's a slightly finer finishing powder that is generally more reflective to light and therefore doesn't show up too obviously on film.

 **smart choice**

I'd recommend a pressed powder with a removable puff for day-to-day touch-ups and a setting spray for special occasions when you want your makeup to stay looking fresh for longer.

pro tip

Buy two pressed powders: one slightly darker than your natural skin colour and one slightly lighter. Then you can use these two colours as a light contouring duo that is suitable for daytime – it will give you a softly contoured look. See Contouring on page 106 to find out how.

self tanning

It's become really popular to fake tan, and there are several options for getting the right bronze for your budget and timeframe. The sun does 80 per cent of the damage to our skin with UV light, so we really want to avoid this – but we love looking tanned. So these are all ways in which you can have that golden glow without the usual wrinkles that either the sun or a tanning bed would give you.

The most important thing to remember is to exfoliate your body first as this will make your tan last longer because it removes a lot of the dead skin cells. You don't want your new tan just washing itself off down the shower, and exfoliating should give you an extra couple of days of tan.

spray tan

Requires you to strip off in a little booth while someone with an air gun sprays you all over with a tanning liquid. It may contain dihydroxyacetone (DHA), so definitely try not to breathe it in! It comes in light (10 per cent DHA), medium (12 per cent) and dark (14 per cent) and should go on fairly evenly.

Spray tans last about three to six days and do not provide any protection from the sun – it's fake, remember! Another downside is that, depending on what brand of tan is used and the skill of the operator, you may end up with dirty-looking pores where the tint has collected in them. It can quickly add up cost-wise if you are getting it done regularly, so it's best saved for a special occasion.

self-tanning gel, crème or mousse

Good for applying yourself at home, these are convenient, fairly inexpensive and last about six days. The smell, ease of application and results all vary quite considerably. Apply them either with a mitt or by hand, but keep in mind that you will need to wash your hands completely afterwards to avoid the dreaded brown palms! And you may need to enlist a friend to help as it's sometimes tricky to reach your back.

instant colour spray

These are great if you need colour right now. As in, instant. Clue's in the name, right? They usually come in an aerosol can and spray out a liquid that's a bit like a foundation onto your chosen area. They rub off on clothing, which is a pain, but are handy if you just need tanned legs for the day. They do look good when applied correctly and can be washed off.

bronzing crème

These are great if you have a little colour already and you just want to enhance it and possibly add a golden glow. They do come off quite a bit on clothing, so be careful, but they're cheap, effective and rinse off in the shower.

bronzing powder

Get out your largest powder brush and start bronzing! Bronzing powder is good for smaller body parts and can add a bit of sparkle or shimmer, but is time consuming if you're trying to do large portions of your body and it does come off easily on clothing. The flipside is it washes straight off in the shower!

things you *think* you may need – but you really don't

Cosmetic houses are excellent at getting you to buy multiples of the same or similar products just by giving them different names to make you think you need them all. Here are three examples. These three products are basically all the same thing: their main ingredient is silicone with various degrees of shine. So at the end of the day, you only need to buy one.

primers

Primers are marketed for use underneath foundations to help the foundation last longer and go on more smoothly. They are primarily made of silicone, which sits on top of the skin to create a waterproof barrier and fill in fine lines and pores. But what most people don't realise is that many liquid foundations already contain a silicone built into the formula to help with a smooth application.

If you have a special occasion and you want your makeup to last longer, especially if you have oily skin, then a primer can help to enhance the performance and durability of your makeup. I just don't think it's worth wearing every day – if my foundation or moisturiser already includes a silicone, to me that's just doubling up. So look for dimethicone, dimethiconecopolyol, dimethiconol, cyclomethicone, methicone or phenyl trimethicone, or in the ingredient lists of your foundation or moisturiser to know.

pore-minimising creams

You cannot change the size of your pores; they are what they are. You've probably inherited them from your parents. What you can do, though, is keep your skin clean and exfoliate lightly twice a week. When oil and dirt collect in a pore it appears larger, so keeping pores clean will make them appear smaller. Simple, right?

Many pore-minimising creams contain silicone. Silicone will fill in the pores temporarily and allow makeup to sit on top of them but it's not a permanent solution. So, instead of splashing out on yet another product, give your cleaning routine some extra minutes each week.

shine-reducing creams

So, you have shiny skin – lucky you! This means your oil supplies are working overtime and that's great for keeping your skin lubricated. However, if you don't want to be super shiny then the cosmetic giants have created just the thing for you: shine-reducing creams. Again, though, these contain silicone which effectively blocks the oil from coming out of your pores by painting a veil on top of them.

I'd recommend using these silicone creams only occasionally and doing a clay mask a couple of times a week instead. You can't stop your skin producing oil; it's what it is supposed to do. You can only manage the issue. And if you continually strip your skin of oil with astringent toners, you will end up with a bigger problem. Try to look at oily skin from a new angle: it is your friend and will make you look younger in the long term, plus dewy skin is younger skin!

my advice? just buy a good, cheap matt primer and it should do all three jobs at once: make your foundation last longer, disguise large pores and minimise shine . . .

. . . Try not to be hypnotised by the colourful packaging and instead look for one with a silicone in the first three ingredients – though you might need a magnifying glass for that! Then pick whether you want an illuminating one or a more matt one based on your natural level of shine. Simple.

eye creams

Why do we think we actually need an expensive and somehow different cream for under our eyes? Yes, the skin there is a little thinner but luckily if our brains aren't we can realise that essentially, it's the same skin that's all over our faces. If you have dark circles and bags under your eyes this could be due to many causes but fatigue is the most common, so have a read of my tips on sleep and relaxation (see pages 72–73 and 76–77). As long as your usual moisturiser or oil doesn't contain possible eye irritants – like alcohol, which is drying, or fragrance, which can be irritating – then all good.

If you're happy to be sucked in by the marketing and you feel better by putting a different cream there, then knock yourself out. If not, try a couple of warm chamomile teabags or cold cucumber slices on your tired, closed eyes with a ten-minute lie-down – you'll probably end up with the same result or an even better one, not just for your skin but for your bank account.

toners

There used to be the three mantras of skincare: cleanse, tone and moisturise. I think they're embedded in most of our minds. I get the first and last ones, but I just don't see any use for the middle one. A toner is supposed to help cleanse but if your cleanser is any good, you've already done that job. Toner is supposed to restore the pH balance of your skin but your skin is capable of doing that on its own. Sorry, not sold . . . like, at all.

To top it off, many toners contain alcohol, which will irritate your skin and eventually dry it out. That's why I give toner a big miss. If I want to feel the cool freshness of a liquid on my face after I've cleansed, I just use water – or, if I'm feeling super special, a bit of mineral water spray will do the job nicely.

hair removal

laser

I've never had laser hair removal done, but I'm tempted each time I look down at my hairy legs! For those who don't know what it is, it involves permanently removing the hair from a part of the body with a series of laser sessions focused on that area of the skin. Laser is most successful on light skin with dark hair, as dark hair contains more melanin and the laser needs to use that melanin to kill the hair follicle, which it does with light rays. In other words, if you're a blonde then there is probably little point in getting it done as it won't work. In order for laser to have a long-term effect you need to go back about half a dozen times. It can be used anywhere on the body but it can be expensive and sometimes causes skin irritation and burning.

waxing

Waxing can be done in a few different ways. One is to go to a beautician where they will place warm wax onto the area, then place a strip of cloth or paper on the wax and very quickly rip all the hairs out in one go, tearing against the grain of the growth. YOW. It generally lasts about four weeks, so it's not permanent – though you may be permanently scarred by the pain!

An alternative is to go to a beautician who uses hard wax – a thicker wax that doesn't need to be heated up as much, and supposedly doesn't stick to the skin. It is used without cloth or paper and is generally thought to be less painful than strip waxing. It is good for the underarms, bikini line or anywhere else you may be sensitive. You're also likely to be more

susceptible to pain around the time of your period, so try and plan your waxing around that (plus there's the added risk of a tampon string getting caught in the wax . . . !). Your pain tolerance is said to be at its highest following the end of your period until just prior to ovulation.

Speaking of an area that is frequently waxed . . . I recently did a little survey on what sort of 'style' different women had for their pubic hair. I found it differed by age. Woman over forty tended to have just a short back and sides – in other words, just a little trim around the edges. Women in their thirties had the landing strip: just a line up the middle, trimmed short. And women in their twenties had nothing . . . as in, bald. All gone. Interesting, hey! Fashion, it works in weird ways.

With both of these waxes there are home kits available. And they can be used anywhere on the body.

hair removal creams

These sound great but in effect the chemicals in the creams can leave your skin burnt and blistered. I was once having a romantic shower with a partner when he asked me to place some of this cream onto his back because we were going to the beach. So I did, and then I had to scrape the creamy white hairy 'worms' into the shower with the little scraper they give you in the box – yucko. Then I had to redo it because there was still lots of hair left! He ended up practically crying because the cream was stinging him so badly – yep, blisters, lots of them. After that he wore a rash vest and left the hair to poke through the lycra. Super attractive . . . not.

at the end
of the day, it's
personal choice.

shaving

Shaving is certainly convenient. Forgot to shave your legs? It just takes five minutes. The options are a lady shaver, which is a battery-powered shaver that can run over your legs and armpits in seconds, or a handheld razor, which will take a bit longer. Shaving is affordable but you need to repeat it often – every few days or week, depending on how fast your hair grows. The other negative is possible ingrown hairs, so to try to combat them exfoliate your legs before shaving and shave after a warm bath or shower.

Forget about buying dedicated shaving creams for your body as they are a waste of money. Just moisturise afterwards with an alcohol-free cream. If you have particularly dry legs, you can even shave with a light moisturiser on, though it will clog up your blade much faster, so you will need a bowl of warm water to rinse your blade in.

threading

Threading is as old as time and is believed to have originated in the Middle East. A thread is doubled over and then rolled across the surface of the area where hair removal is required. The thread pulls out multiple hairs at once. It is generally only used on the face; it would take forever to thread your legs! It is a reasonably natural form of hair removal plus it's affordable and about as painful as tweezing quickly. But a skilled operator is needed to ensure that you don't end up without any eyebrows!

tweezing

Tweezing is effectively ripping the hair out of the root and is generally only used on the face. It lasts a week or so. For most people it's not that painful but if you do find it is, get an ice cube and place it on the target before tweezing – it helps numb the area. It is always easier to tweeze with a good, sharp and balanced pair of tweezers (available from most chemists). I like to use angled tweezers as I find it easier to be precise with them. They are also handy for placing false eyelashes (see page 126).

botox and other instant fixes

the most cosmetically enhanced countries are the usa, followed by brazil, then japan.

I'm not the type of woman who goes under the knife, but I certainly don't judge those who do. I'm not a celebrity and I'm not a model. I don't live that life and my work doesn't depend on my looks, thank goodness. I'm not going to cling to my youth but I'm not prepared to discard it easily either – I'll hang on determinedly while I slowly embrace my age. I'll work just as hard on my inner beauty, but also try to prevent ageing with a healthy lifestyle. That's the key to real and sustainable beauty.

Beauty certainly means different things to different cultures. The one I'm living in

seems to love plastic surgery. But that's not for me; I don't want to be sliced and diced. I like a face with character and movement, it's beautiful. There's no point in lying about it – I can see if you've had botox from 20 metres. Having said that, I don't think it's anything to be ashamed of and I think it's kind of funny that we feel we need to lie about it.

Botox is from the family of botulinum toxins, which are some of the most lethal substances known to man. Yet we inject them into our faces to cause slight paralysis of the muscles and therefore appear to have fewer wrinkles. It's kind of crazy, really, yet it's become a very common beauty aid, with over 4.6 million Americans being injected in 2017 alone. We don't formally record the statistics for botox here in Australia, but I dare say we are similar in our love for an instant fix. Cost is a big factor with botox, as it needs to be repeated about every four months and can be $350 – $700 per visit depending on the quantity that's injected.

The other popular procedure that is on the rise is dermal fillers to puff up your lips or fill in facial lines. We've all seen the very bee-stung lips that are everywhere now. Like botox, they are expensive to get and maintain – in fact they are almost twice as expensive, though they do last double the time period, with top-ups required about every eight months.

Also very popular is liposuction, where the fat literally gets sucked out of your body with what looks like a vacuum cleaner, but by far the most in-demand invasive procedures for women are breast augmentation followed by nose jobs and eyelid surgery. Women make up nearly 86 per cent of the customers. (The most popular procedure for men is a nose job, while Germany leads the pack in the number of penile implants – by inches.)

If you do decide to get botox, don't go to a botox party where you'll be encouraged to drink champagne and everyone will get injected by who knows whom. Do your homework and go to someone reputable – sober.

When shopping around, try to see other results from that same surgeon as it may give you a good indication of how things will turn out. Most importantly, do your research. There are many people performing botox injections, so make sure that they are actually qualified. I wouldn't want my eye drooping because of a misplaced needle.

I believe that you are responsible for and in control of your own body. If you want plastic surgery then knock yourself out. If you want a facelift, again, it's your choice. The only thing I would ask is why you are doing it: is it for you or for someone else? Because I think that if we focused on our inner beauty must-haves like confidence and kindness first, we might look at getting these procedures done in a very different light and realise that they're perhaps not as important to our sense of self as we're made to think they are.

tools of the trade

When applying makeup, having the right tools makes it easier to get great results, so here are the key ones I rely on. You don't need to splash out anything expensive – there are many good brushes and sponges available that are completely affordable.

The basic rule I use is acrylic bristles for any brush that I'm going to be washing often (like a foundation brush) and Taklon bristles for the ones I'm not, such as powder brushes. I wash brushes that are used with wet cosmetics more regularly because the moisture content encourages bacteria to grow, which I definitely don't want. I wash my personal brushes weekly and it also helps

the colour cosmetic to go on cleanly when I am applying. As both acrylic and Taklon are synthetic, they're animal-friendly – and they also tend to be cheaper than natural brushes.

When cleaning my brushes, I just use my antibacterial dish washing detergent – it's cheap and effective. Many brush cleaners that you buy are alcohol-based and may therefore deteriorate your brushes more quickly. To dry, try to hang them with the head facing down or lie them flat, as this will help to reduce the amount of moisture that gets in between the bottom of the brush head and the handle, which may make the brush rot.

1 and 2: foundation/primer and buffer brushes

I recommend a dome-shaped brush with acrylic bristles for foundation and primer. I also like a flat-headed buffing brush for when I want a little less makeup on my face: first I apply foundation and then I grab my buffer brush and buff away in circular motions on my face. It removes any excess, plus it's almost like a little massage!

3 and 4: latex sponges

Makeup sponges come in all shapes and sizes but the ones I go for are the triangle-shaped ones made of latex plus the very small teardrop-shaped ones. The first of these are good for buffing your foundation after application – they push it into your skin and remove excess for a more flawless look. Some people use them to apply foundation and they do work just as well as a brush, but be aware the sponge will soak up a fair amount of foundation so you tend to waste more this way. The smaller teardrop sponges are good for applying concealer around the eye area.

5 and 6: concealer brushes

I have two of these, both acrylic for frequent washing: an angled one to get in around the eye area and a domed one for everywhere else.

7 and 8: highlighting brushes

A fan brush is good for powder highlighter, or possibly a smaller angled brush when I want to be more precise. I often use my finger when applying a cream highlighter.

9: angled brush

I use an angled brush for applying contouring creams onto the face as the shape makes contouring easier and more precise. I'd recommend one with a fairly firm head, preferably acrylic.

10: blusher brush

I either use a smaller rounded powder brush or my angled brush (above) for applying blusher or bronzer. If I'm doing lots of bronzing I may use a larger, rounded powder brush to cover the area more effectively, whereas if I want to be precise I use one that's smaller and more angled.

11–15: eyeshadow brushes

There are five that I cannot live without. First, a smaller brush with a domed Taklon head for general application. Then a pair of blending brushes: one with a rounded head, the other a smaller, angled blending brush to get into tricky areas and create a great eye flick. Finally, two eyeshadow contour brushes for using on the socket line, one domed and one rounded.

16 and 17: eyeliner brushes

Again, I use a smaller, firm-headed angled brush – it needs to be firm to create a clean line. A really fine-tipped brush is also a must-have for drawing on super thin eyeliner.

18: lash comb

Use to comb through your lashes to separate them for better definition (*before* your mascara is dry, otherwise you might pull out lashes – and no one wants that!).

19: eyebrow brush

I like to use a firm, angled brush which has a spool at the other end of it so I can quickly swap between the two while I am working. I brush the brows up with the spool and then fill with the angled brush.

20: lip brush

I like a short, square, firm lip brush that I can turn on its side to draw a clean line around the outline of the lips. The rule with these is the larger the lips, the larger the brush.

21–25: powder and body brushes

I use a variety; smaller brushes (rectangular and fan-shaped) are best for applying powder strategically, while bigger ones are good for bronzer, highlighter and even coverage of large areas. A kabuki brush (24) is excellent for blending.

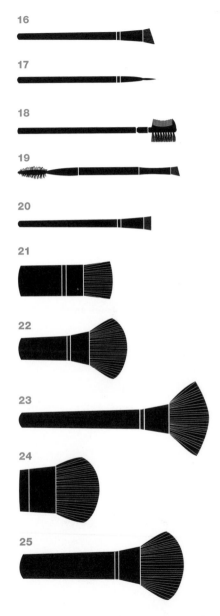

beauty hacks

alternative ways of using
the makeup you already own:

- Use your lipstick as a blush or even as a crème eyeshadow
- Top off your eyeshadow with a highlighting powder to make it pop
- Use your eyeshadows with a wet brush as an eyeliner
- Apply concealer under your lipstick to change the colour
- Mix pressed powder with your powder blush to lighten it
- Brush highlighting powder on top of your blush to make your cheeks glow
- Use your crème blush as a lipstick
- Mix moisturiser in with your foundation to make it more sheer
- Mix your eyeshadow with loose powder to lighten the colour
- Layer different coloured lipsticks to make new shades
- Layer eyeshadow on top of your eyeliner to build new colours
- Apply your eyeshadow with a wet brush like a watercolour paint for a more intense look
- Use a light eyeshadow on top of lipstick in the centre of your lips to create more of a pout
- Touch up your dark roots or grey hairs with mascara
- Blot and lightly powder your glossy lipstick to turn it matt

references

Axelsson, J., Sundelin, T., Ingre, M., et al., 'Beauty Sleep: Experimental Study on the Perceived Health and Attractiveness of Sleep Deprived People', *BMJ*, 2010; 341(c6614), DOI: https://doi.org/10.1136/bmj.c6614.

Bissett, D., Oblong, J., Berge, C., 'Niacinamide: A B Vitamin that Improves Aging Facial Skin Appearance', *Dermatologic Surgery*, 2005, 31(7 Pt 2): 860–5.

Bratman, G. N., Hamilton, J. P., Hahn, K. S., et al., 'Nature Reduces Rumination and sgPFC Activation', *Proceedings of the National Academy of Sciences*, 2015, 112(28): 8567–72. DOI: 10.1073/pnas.1510459112.

Burgess, C., 'Topical vitamins', *J Drugs Dermatol.*, 2008, 7(7 Suppl): s2–6.

Cancer Council, 'Vitamin D', https://www.cancer.org.au/preventing-cancer/sun-protection/vitamin-d/.

Ghevariya, V., Singhal, S., Anand, S., 'The Skin: A Mirror to the Gut', *Int J Colorectal Dis*, 2013, 28: 889. DOI: https://doi.org/10.1007/s00384-012-1637-x.

Kim, S. A., Hagan, K. A., Grodstein, F., et al., 'Optimism and Cause-Specific Mortality: A Prospective Cohort Study', *American Journal of Epidemiology*, 2017, 185(1): 21–29. DOI: 10.1093/aje/kww182.

Kozaki, T., Horinouchi, K., Noguchi, J., et al., '1–7 Physiological Effects of Bathing in the Forest Atmosphere (II)-Blood Pressure and Heart Rate Variability', *Journal of Physiological Anthropology and Applied Human Science*, 2005, 24(2): 188–189.

Knutson, K. L., 'Impact of Sleep and Sleep Loss on Glucose Homeostasis and Appetite Regulation', *Sleep Medicine Clinics*, 2007, 2(2): 187–197. DOI: https://doi.org/10.1016/j.jsmc.2007.03.004.

Lyyra, T.-M., Törmäkangas, T. M., Read, S., et al., 'Satisfaction with Present Life Predicts Survival in Octogenarians', *The Journals of Gerontology: Series B*, 2006, 61(6): P319–P326. DOI: 10.1093/geronb/61.6.P319.

Medical Observer, 'How a Healthy Diet Affects the Gut Microbiome', https://www.medicalobserver.com.au/medical-news/nutrition/how-a-healthy-diet-affects-the-gut-microbiome.

Morselli, L., et al., 'Role of Sleep Duration in the Regulation of Glucose Metabolism and Appetite', *Best Practice & Research Clinical Endocrinology & Metabolism*, 2010, 24(5): 687–702. DOI: 10.1016/j.beem.2010.07.005.

National Rosacea Society, 'Factors That May Trigger Rosacea Flare-Ups', https://www.rosacea.org/patients/materials/triggers.php.

National Eczema Association, 'Eczema Causes and Triggers', https://nationaleczema.org/eczema/causes-and-triggers-of-eczema/.

Riley, J. L. 3rd, Robinson, M. E., Wise, E A., Price, D. D., 'A Meta-Analytic Review of Pain Perception Across the Menstrual Cycle', *Pain*, 1999, 81(3): 225–35.

Sharma, A., Madaan, V., Petty, F. D., 'Exercise for Mental Health', *Primary Care Companion to The Journal of Clinical Psychiatry*, 2006, 8(2): 106.

SunSmart, 'How Much Sun is Enough?', http://www.sunsmart.com.au/downloads/resources/brochures/how-much-sun-enough-vitamin-d.pdf.

Van den Berg, M. M. H. E., Maas, J., Muller, R., et al., 'Autonomic Nervous System Responses to Viewing Green and Built Settings: Differentiating Between Sympathetic and Parasympathetic Activity', *International Journal of Environmental Research and Public Health*, 2015, 12(12): 15860–15874. DOI: 10.3390/ijerph121215026.

Vighi, G., Marcucci, F., Sensi, L., et al., 'Allergy and the Gastrointestinal System', *Clinical and Experimental Immunology*, 2008, 153(Suppl 1): 3–6. DOI: http://doi.org/10.1111/j.1365-2249.2008.03713.x.

Yosipovitch, G., Tang, M., Dawn, A. G., et al., 'Study of Psychological Stress, Sebum Production and Acne Vulgaris in Adolescents', *Acta Derm Venereol*, 2007, 87(2): 135–9. DOI: 10.2340/00015555-0231.

thanks to

Claire Fisers, Lilli Langendoen, Terence Langendoen, Myrtle Jeffs, Lisa Tyler, Ashley Barbieri, Virginia Sutton, Kylie Starling, all the girls at Coco Productions for helping with my beauty career, Zoe King and all of the hardworking people at The Blair Partnership, Izzy Yates and Lou Ryan at Penguin Random House Australia, all of the models and celebs that have chatted to me over the years plus the many cosmetics chemists and cosmetics companies I have talked to and worked for.

follow bernadette online

simplybern.com

also available as an e-book